# HOW TO NOT BE A MONSTER

## THE IMPACT OF YOGA ON WORK, PLAY, AND FAMILY

STEFANE BARBEAU

Author photograph by Ken Dundas. Author portrait illustration by Denis Barbeau. All other illustrations by Stefane Barbeau.

First printing: 2020

Clinic Yoga Media, 2799 North Girasol Avenue, Palm Springs, CA 92262 www.clinic.yoga

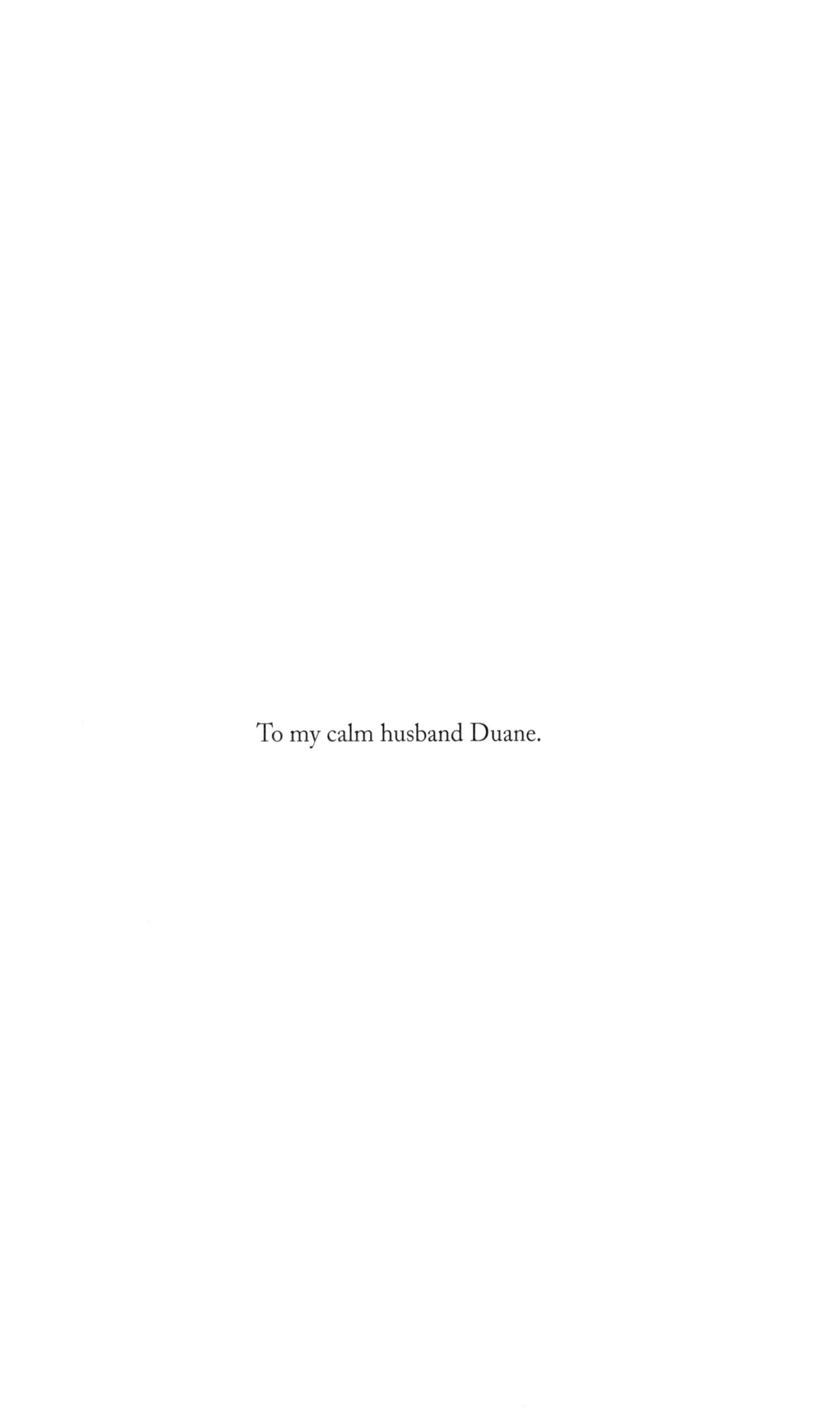

To my calm husband Duane.

**LET'S BEGIN** **7**
WHY YOGA? 10
WHY ME? 14
WHY THIS BOOK? 19

**MOTIVATION** **25**
GAMENESS 29
PROCRASTINATION 32
DISCIPLINE 35
EQUANIMITY 38
EXPECTATIONS 43
MINDFULNESS 46
A STUDIO 50
PLEASURE 54
PATIENCE 58

**LEARNING** **63**
COMMUNICATION 67
WORDS 69
A CLASS 77
A STUDENT 80
A TEACHER 84
STUNTED 89
CULTURE 91
PRACTICE 94
TRAINING 99
A PLATEAU 102
MEMORY 104

**HEALTH** **107**
RESILIENCE 111
POSTURE 116
BREATHING 119

CHANTING 124
PHYSIOLOGY 127
STRENGTH, FLEXIBILITY, AND BALANCE 132
PAIN 137
INJURY 140
RECOVERY 143
REST 151
POLLUTION 156

**CHANGE 159**
A CRISIS 163
TRANSFORMATION 165
A BREAKTHROUGH 167
AGE 169
SIMPLICITY 177
COMFORT 180
CREATIVITY 183

**EGO 189**
GRATITUDE 195
SNEAKINESS 199
VULNERABILITY 203
TRUST 206
PERFECTION 209
SPIRITUALITY 212
FEAR 214
CONFIDENCE 218
SELF-AWARENESS 221
AWARENESS PRACTICE 223

**LET'S FINISH 225**
CHEAT SHEET 230

# LET'S BEGIN

Maybe you've bought this book because the title resonates with you. Maybe you've startled yourself with how poorly you interacted with a loved one or colleague and are trying to understand why. Maybe you have negative thoughts that will just not leave your head. Maybe you're struggling to make sense of the path of indulgent destruction that lies behind you, and you're worried about what lies ahead. Or maybe you're just interested in yoga. Or maybe all of the above, and you suspect you might be a monster who needs help. But that's hard to admit, so rest easy. I'll take the mantle: I'm a monster. I won't mention you again.

In stories, a monster is an imaginary creature that is typically large, ugly, and frightening, with a disregard for those in its midst, except for possibly an interest in eating them. A monster is a mess of impulses that leads to no good.

Every day, I feel competitive, jealous, angry, indulgent, and reactionary. I bear a festering grudge for a neighbor who caused problems while we built our house. I think through detailed plans for what I would say and do to a former employer who I feel mistreated me twenty years ago. I imagine a driver who has cut me off losing control of his car and driving into a telephone pole. Upon hearing that an acquaintance has achieved some form of success, I stun myself with an immediate reaction of hope for them to fail. When I was a kid, my temper was so bad that my parents would warn me of the realities of what I might turn into as an adult: a monster. I'd fly into a frenzy of fists and feet with older kids at the slightest taunt. I'd scream bloody murder if my brother wasn't cooperating with me. My mother once had to send a friend home from a playdate because he wasn't drawing the way I wanted him to, and I was enraged. I felt sick with regret after each outburst, but it took me a long time for that feeling to be enough to prevent me from lashing out again.

And guess what? I'm also often scared, anxious, nervous, and hurt, as monsters usually turn out to be. I worry friends might exclude me from events. I'll waste time on the couch, overwhelmed by thoughts of what I should or could be doing, including things I actually enjoy. I'm in almost constant fear that my and my husband's livelihoods will come to a crashing end and we'll be on the street within a month.

These are dramatic examples, but there are also more subtle thoughts and behaviors flitting through my activities that literally make me shake my head to stave them off. I feel addicted to these tendencies. They feel… pretty good. I've got company: I've seen and heard examples of others—parents, teens, CEOs, yoga masters—behaving like monsters, and sometimes succeeding not just in spite of that, but because of that, only to eventually stumble.

But when I think of myself from ten years ago, I was worse; all of these thoughts and behaviors were just immutable parts of my personality, I figured, and maybe I could mask them, but certainly not fix them. I was unable to see myself as separate from my monster-like tendencies. Now, I can.

I've realized that in the brief moments when I manage to avoid these dark places, I feel better, lighter, unburdened... like I can actually get something constructivc done. I've started to consider the times when I'm a caring, thoughtful and valuable member of society, and realize there are many—far more than the times I've been monstrous.

Yoga has helped me find this relief. It has taught me to create the circumstances I can operate within without being a monster. It takes work, but the payoff is worth it. You might be wondering how it is that by waving my arms and legs around while standing on a rubber mat for an hour a few times a week somehow helps me to achieve a state of well-being and helps me be good. This skepticism is reasonable. Why yoga? I'll try to explain.

## WHY YOGA?

I encounter the question "Why yoga?" often. The easy answer: it keeps me fit and sane. In a nutshell, here's how yoga was designed to work many, many years ago:

**Yoga is a series of movements, the practice of which reduces distractions so that, with a clear head, I can identify, explore, and embrace my true self.**

Easy, huh? More straightforwardly, a yoga practice involves a series of full-body movements that stretch and strengthen my muscles, smooth out my breathing, and ultimately clear my head so that I can get on with life happily and with purpose.

Yoga is a Sanskrit word that means "to yoke". This can be interpreted many ways, but yoga as a "union" of body and mind resonates with me. It's a simple definition that helps to remind me that both aspects of my existence are important and must be cultivated.

**I want to live a long life, so I need to take care of my body, and I want to be happy for that time, so I need to take care of my mind.**

There are many effective ways to address mental and physical fitness: therapy, medication, meditation, gym memberships, and personal trainers. But I've realized that yoga digs deeper and reaches further in the process; yoga is the only approach that is specifically and thoroughly designed to benefit me physically and mentally at the same time.

The physicality of a yoga practice is an obvious connection to a healthy body. I learned in high school biology that exercise is good for me. During a yoga session, I'm moving at a steady pace through a series of postures, or asanas, that are designed to restore or increase muscle strength and flexibility. Controlled breathing paired with movement strengthens my heart, thereby increasing nourishing blood flow to my cells and allowing them to regenerate. This prolongs my youthfulness. This is how there are 80-year-old yoga practitioners who can do handstands.

But the connection of yoga to the mind is less obvious. How does yoga strengthen my mind? Yoga works from the outside in, and from the inside out, as needed. My body is a physical manifestation of my mental state, and vice versa. If I'm depressed, I don't want to use my body, and I slouch and sleep. If I'm angry, my blood pressure increases, and my muscles engage. If I'm inspired, I feel energized and can run a mile without effort. So it stands to reason that altering the state of my body can affect my mind, forcing it to catch up, so to speak. If I sit quietly and focus on breathing slowly, I will relax. Cracking a smile will improve my mood.

The postures I practice in yoga are not arbitrary; they've been developed through years of trial and error. The result is a set of poses that I can rely on to make sure that I'm getting a well-rounded "rebalancing". Some postures are more complex and challenging than others, but that distinction is not for my body—I can stick to the simpler postures and still benefit physically. The more advanced postures are for my brain—overcoming ego, challenging my memory, building focus. Everything I am subjected to (good or bad) has a cumulative effect on me. The yoga mat is a microcosm of the ups and downs of everyday life; by practicing a series of ever-more-challenging yoga postures, I'm working to develop greater resilience and agility.

**Yoga is functional training for living.**

There are extremes of how yoga is conveyed in western culture: it's either a spiritual practice or a gym workout. Unfortunately, if yoga is just treated as a workout, I'm missing out on the richness of its design and therefore its full benefit. Conversely, if it's treated entirely as a spiritual practice, restricted to esoteric and elusive theories, it can be exclusive and baffling. The reality is it's a spectrum, and with a little understanding of both ends, I've found what's right for me in yoga and put aside the rest. I have evolved in my practice, depending on my life situation. At times it's been more of a mental practice, and at times more physical. The balance is achieved not just within one practice session, but throughout the course of hours and hours of work on the mat: practice. My mind and body are learning, and without learning, the physical and mental fitness that I'm achieving from one day to the next are not sustainable.

A few years ago, I met a friend of a friend at a weekend getaway in San Francisco. During meals, he kept popping outside to smoke. This was not unusual, nor was listening to him hacking at two in the morning. But the next day during breakfast, he started talking about health. He said he smoked because he liked it, and he was "not afraid of dying." At the time I took this as a heavy and rather thoughtful justification for letting his pleasurable habit affect his health.

But afterwards, I realized fear of death is not what encourages me to practice healthy living; an enjoyment of life and a will to live as long as possible does. My friend wasn't afraid to die, but maybe he was struggling to learn how to live.

**I don't practice yoga to get better at yoga.
I practice yoga to get better at living.**

As I've explored my practice, I've discovered deeper answers to "why yoga?", depending on circumstances. Yoga is a way to undo the days, weeks, months, years, or decades of damage my body and mind have accumulated. Yoga is a way to prepare for the future. Yoga is a balance of acceptance and ambition. Yoga is a process of discovery. Yoga is an opportunity to search for, explore, and then to be my true self.

## WHY ME?

When I was five years old, I wanted to be an artist. I still do. I studied product design in university and upon graduating moved immediately into the consulting world. A few years in, I co-founded, with my partner whom I had met in school, a design, manufacturing, and distribution company. We garnered quite a bit of industry recognition in the form of awards and press coverage. We were accomplishing more than what we had set out to and felt quite successful. Then the economic collapse of 2008 was upon us, and much of what we had built was on the verge of evaporating. I had a very tenuous hold on my identity because it had been so deeply enmeshed with the company I had helped build.

In parallel, I attended my first yoga class in 1999 while living in Boston. Friends were visiting from out of town. The night before, one of them boozed us into agreeing to a hot yoga class she had located for the next morning. Yes, my first yoga experience was because of a drunken dare. I figured by the next morning nobody would be up to it anyway, but I was wrong. The next thing I knew I was face-down on a yoga mat, gasping for air in the super-heated basement room of an old building in Roslindale, along with forty other people of different shapes, sizes and ages, all crammed foot-to-face... and I went back to this studio pretty regularly for two years. Something had clicked. This was the first time I had committed to something athletic. (I was a person who'd be sore from playing video games.) I loved the discipline of this yoga. I loved the feeling of accomplishment. If only high school gym class could have been like this, I thought painfully. I was tracking changes in my flexibility and strength: I could squat for longer periods, and I could get my face closer to my knees each time I bent forward. I could balance on one foot, with the other extended behind me. Amid the soaked towels and grunting bodies, I found a focus and a mental stamina I didn't know I had.

My partner, Duane, often practiced with me. A couple of years into going to this studio, after a particularly intense day dealing with suppliers and customers he said, "I'm too stressed to go to yoga."

Ah. We laughed about it, but he was right. The time commitment and the odd performance anxiety that were creeping in were turning it into an unpleasant experience. As many things go, I drifted away from this practice that until a couple of months before had seemed like a lifelong commitment. Life and work got in the way, and I went less and less often, and then I stopped.

A few years later I started practicing yoga twice a week at a gym. None of the classes were even close to as difficult as the hot yoga from before, but that was okay. This sparked my interest again. Duane gave me a yoga book for my birthday.

In 2010, after a couple of years of grinding through a soul-sucking economy and a variety of physical and mental traumas, we sold our company. This was the first of many "fuck it" moments we had experienced, and it felt good. Duane was offered a leadership position at a sports apparel company, and we said goodbye to our shocked friends and moved to Hong Kong. By sheer coincidence I discovered a large Indian yoga community there. I had the luxury of free time—we were there on an expat package—and I spent two years immersed in yoga, sometimes taking up to three classes a day, including teacher certification courses. We moved back to North America in 2012, and I continued teaching yoga, at first in other studios and then eventually in my own.

In my forty-ninth year, I'm now physically and mentally healthier than I was at eighteen. I've had open-heart surgery to repair a congenital valve defect. I've been through two financial crises. I've been through father loss. I've been through decades-long family addiction secrets, anxiety, and depression, and yoga has helped rebuild my fitness and sanity. I'm a better person, friend, son, and husband than I was, despite the crises: more empathetic, and more resilient. And I've realized that's the baseline of what I need to live a good life. We had been quite successful with our product distribution business, but once I discovered the value of learning and teaching yoga, I realized this:

**Throughout my career, I had been confusing success with fulfillment.**

That being said, I have no regrets about my career path; had I not lived in Boston designing products, I never would have wound up in Hong Kong, and perhaps my yoga career would not have started.

I still do design work periodically, and it's also valuable and cost-effective to have full creative control over how my yoga business is presented. Yoga has in fact informed my design work; it has brought some form to my creative process and helped me pause and think when a gut check is necessary. I often travel to corporations and schools to lead workshops on creative leadership, and yoga is always used to illustrate the importance of a solid process of learn-test-refine. And when people hear I teach yoga, the conversation gets easier and more relaxed. It's more human.

Right now, I'm focused on the practical impact of a yoga practice more than on the depth of study that's available; the Sanskrit, history, and philosophy are there for me to address if I want, but arguably it's not valuable unless there's first-hand experience with a dedicated practice. I know the intended benefits, and I believe they're achievable because I can see results in myself and in the people I teach.

Yoga has become a lifelong practice for me, finally, because I see its depth. Its inherence as a practice means there's no end to its novelty or challenges, nor to its benefits. Yoga helps me learn about myself, and since I'm always changing—aging, experiencing, failing, succeeding—there's a never-ending supply of material to sort through on the yoga mat. Yoga has helped show that I am worth a lot, and that I can accomplish a great deal if I persevere, roll with the punches, and dig a little deeper every day.

## WHY THIS BOOK?

This book is about why, if I could only choose one physical activity, it would be yoga. If I could only choose one form of therapy, given the myriad options of life coaching, behavioral therapy, psychology, and psychiatry, I would choose yoga. If I could only choose one way to pass the time and feel engaged, constructive, and fulfilled, I would choose yoga. If everything were collapsing around me, and I were the last person on earth, I would literally still practice yoga.

Beyond that, it's challenging to give more detail about why yoga is important to me without being boring, arrogant, preachy, or muddled. There are some pretty good answers to "Why yoga?" out there that I agree with, but they're based heavily on ancient texts, the Yoga Sutras, and the reality of context makes the content unrelatable without significant research and discussion.

**The accessibility of yoga as a practice is at odds with its inaccessibility as a study.**

Nonetheless, a regular yoga practice has deepened my understanding of my monster self. It has given me tools that, off the mat—in real life—help me solve otherwise paralyzing problems, interact thoughtfully with others, and lead a healthy, constructive existence.

This book stems entirely from my own yoga practice. Some of the insights and stories might not seem yoga-related, or that they could not have been learned through yoga, but there is still a connection for me, if merely that the thought came to me on the mat.

**The self-reflective nature of yoga has opened me to think more broadly about my life and my place in the world.**

I know that yoga is good for me mentally and physically, but I'm only starting to understand the depth of why and how. The process of compiling my observations in a meaningful and organized way has deepened my understanding of yoga's benefits, and has also given me better answers at parties. Hopefully you'll get some good answers from this book too.

It's challenging to sustain my yoga practice consistently; I experience good feelings during and afterwards, but I hesitate to start almost every time. But when I'm able to reflect on an activity by writing or reading about it, I find value that justifies the effort, and this motivates me to keep it up. I'm at a point in life where I'm looking for meaning in what I do. The insights I derive from my yoga practice often make me stop and think, "Wow—this is useful. I need to tell someone." I have found, as I teach yoga, that many people are also starved for meaning. Books are a chance to learn, reflect, find inspiration, and to make those connections in a private, quiet setting.

So here it is: a document of relatable, yoga-inspired insights, anecdotes, and exercises. This is for yoga enthusiasts, beginner or advanced, looking for deeper self-awareness and meaning from their practice. And it's also for non-yogis; the insights apply to real life, you don't require the context of a yoga practice, nor a bookshelf of yoga texts to find this book useful. There are eight limbs, or facets, of yoga that encapsulate general guidelines for leading a happy, healthy life. Those limbs each branch off into several deeper ideas. There are decades worth of study available. So the experiences I'm communicating in this book are just scratching the surface of the opportunity for transformation that yoga presents in all the available literature and teaching.

**All that's required to find this book valuable is to start to see life as a practice.**

I've been careful to write everything from my own perspective, and therefore "I" comes up a lot. This may be a little awkward to read at first, and it took effort to overcome the urge to tell people "we do this" or "you feel this." But that's not up to me; I'm offering my own insights for readers to use as guidance and to apply to their own experiences as they see fit. I can't presume more.

I've divided this book into five sections: Motivation, Learning, Health, Change and Ego. This breakdown and order reflects my journey onto the yoga mat every day, from the willingness to even do a practice, to what I discover while practicing, including its impact on my physical and mental health, to the transformations I've witnessed in myself and others, and finally, to the more fundamental understanding of my actions and reactions as an emotional human being. Very simply: throughout my day, on and off my yoga mat, there's an ongoing exchange between my body and my mind that I can tune into to become a better person—more self-aware, more empathetic. Often, when I'm not at my best, it's because there's a rift in that dynamic. Who's in charge? This is when I tend to be a monster: a victim to my impulses to act or not act in the worst of ways, not to listen but to assume, to plow forward blindly only to later be filled with regret. Strengthening the connection of my mind to my body helps to un-monster me.

Are you ready? Take a breath. Let's begin.

# MOTIVATION

A student told me they sometimes dread coming to a session. But they still come, perhaps because they know they'll still have to pay if they don't! Hopefully, the real reason is they have proof that when they're finished, they feel better than when they arrived and they're glad they came.

Getting on the yoga mat is hard. I've asked myself how I can help students manage their motivation. The best answer, I have found, is a paradox: not to look explicitly for motivation, be it a positive emotion associated with a good experience, or an urgency to achieve a certain goal. Instead, taking a step back from the emotions associated with an activity, be they positive or negative, and just observing the sensations—is what suits me best. But this mindset—equanimity—is challenging to cultivate.

I often have positive emotional reactions to physical and mental activities like yoga. Yes, the feeling can sometimes motivate me to keep going, but the problem is, when I'm between sessions, that feeling fades quickly, and it's hard to conjure it on demand.

**Emotions are an unreliable tool—there one moment and gone the next.**

But if I disconnect a reaction, positive or negative, from an activity, then approaching that activity the next time is actually less burdensome. I'm not anticipating torture, nor am I setting myself up to expect joy from this new experience to match or surpass the previous one. Amid fond or bad memories, I find it helpful to remind myself the next time will be different, and an opportunity to experience yet another set of reactions to broaden my self-awareness.

There is a lot to deal with in a seventy-five-minute yoga session. It's physically and mentally exhausting. So how do I keep at it? I take note of the positive results off the mat, whether it's lower blood pressure, a clear head, more calmness in tense situations, or simply not being achy when I get out of bed. These are not emotional states, they're physical observations, and they're plenty motivational to return to the mat each time. An emotional detachment from the discomfort of some of the postures is needed to get through a yoga session. That same equanimity is what I need to get back to the mat each time.

Outsiders can help with motivation. As a teacher, I've learned to limit my compliments of students on their achievement and to focus on their progress. This is grade-school teaching 101, but it holds true just as much for adults, in fact perhaps more so: I can't think of many times in my pre-yoga career when a manager took the time to describe my progress in a constructive, thoughtful way. I imagine that's the case for most people; the hope is to meet performance goals, and to get the yearly bonus, rather than to spend time in the weeds of self-reflection on how they got there. With my students, I set a realistic goal that is just beyond their current capacity, have them work on it, remind them of their progress and then give them that extra push to meet the goal. Tracking progress is important and has a lasting impact: this can be applied to future endeavors with know-how, ease, and confidence.

So what about task completion? Emotions aside, what about the sheer, practical enormity of some tasks? The end often seems very far off to me, whether it's a three-hour hike or something as straightforward as washing party dishes. I've realized that, especially with big, daunting tasks, if I can make it past the halfway point, then I'm home free. After that, I revel in the mid-point accomplishment, and I reach the finish line without giving it much thought. Yoga confirms this: movement begets more movement, and it inspires me to keep going. But if I don't complete my practice—if I'm distracted mid-way through—I'm left with a strange, unpleasant sense of longing, like I've stopped watching a movie just when the plot was reaching a climax.

Some of my students are motivated by crises. Of course I'm glad they've made it to yoga, but I'm concerned when they're at a breaking point that it's much harder for them to get past their physical or mental limitations, to learn something new and achieve even a tiny bit of transformation. A yoga practice may be beneficial, but for many of them, stacked on top of their already teetering state it can be overwhelming and even counterproductive.

I am motivated by positive results, not panic, pain, pleasure, punishment, or elation. This means taking steps to ensure ongoing wellness at the smooth points in life: when things are going well, when my mind is clear and most receptive to learning. Pain is discouraging, and pleasure is fleeting. Both prevent an objective acknowledgement of progress.

**A clear-headed understanding, with personal evidence, of the benefit of yoga is the best way for me to commit to a practice.**

## GAMENESS

That smiling, relaxed willingness to try something new, to go one more round, to push past the hesitation—I feel that now. But I didn't always. Yoga has taught me to be game.

I used to be that person, who, when faced with a challenge, particularly a public one, would back away and think quietly, "Not for me." I sometimes see this on the yoga mat: in response to my request for a more difficult posture, someone in the session announces, "That's not gonna happen!" They're evidently self-deprecating, and they sometimes get a chuckle from other students, but unfortunately their words have a ripple effect, and they spark the other yogis to lose trust in themselves, and in me.

Since they've brought attention to themselves, and only because of that (I wouldn't normally shine a spotlight on negativity) I gently ask them, "Ah, do you have an injury?" Sometimes they do, and we leave it at that. This is a good point of learning for everyone: if you're injured, don't let ego take over and make you experience more pain. Most of the time, though, they're just scared or embarrassed.

At that point, I encourage them to try alternatives, "just so you can start to feel the beginning of this posture. No more than that." And I wait and look them in the eye. There's a pause as the gears turn in their head, and they realize they're empowered to really address their limitations. Rationally, they have no reason not to try, and they proceed. Within a few seconds, that baby step turns into an adult step and voilà: they're in the posture, without any expectation from me that they do so.

They end the session feeling accomplished and transformed.

I was game when I was a kid. I lost that as I got older. I remember doing cartwheels and flipping over the living room ottoman. I remember standing up on my bicycle seat while I rode. I remember actually being pretty reckless. And then something changed; bad experiences made me fearful of pain and humiliation (also a type of pain.) One time, I twisted my ankle during recess in the second grade and sat with the pain until the end of the day, when I finally, biting back tears and for some reason ashamed, told my teacher. By then my ankle had swollen to double its size, but it was time to go home, and there was nothing she could do. It took weeks to recover, and instructions from my parents and the doctor were, vaguely, don't do that again.

Even now I have a residual sense that my ankle is somehow defective, which I know rationally is not the case. Many of my students have similar issues: an injury from years ago still haunts them mentally and has created a barrier that prevents them from doing certain physical activities. The reality is that with a bit of stretching and strengthening they'd be fine, with no risk of relapse. I see many people who are "out of practice" with trying new things, and the more they avoid, the smaller their world gets. This not only affects them functionally—doing chores, traveling, sleeping—but it can start to affect them socially.

**Yoga is a rare opportunity to dissolve a lifetime's worth of physical and mental barriers.**

My own ongoing training as a yogi has been humbling, and

I've brought gameness to it. I'm never the most flexible, the strongest, the calmest, or the fittest person in the room. I'm often used by master instructors as a test dummy for demonstrating a posture, but they usually use me to show what not to do! I like this role, and earlier on I was surprised by my willingness to basically be humiliated in front of a group of people. But I quickly realized that I was benefiting from this exposure far more than anyone else in the room. Not only was I getting direct, hands-on instructions for a particular posture, but I was being forced to manage and model my own vulnerability.

This has made me reassess my reactions to things off the mat as well. I now realize that shutting something down because of my own fear or ego stunts growth, and it's contagious. It gives me a perverse permission to cater to my fears and to show others how they can too. I ask myself: where else do I allow fear to shut things down? At a wedding reception on the dance floor? With my friends planning a camping trip? If the answer is yes, perhaps I should rethink my approach, because most likely my attitude is not having a good effect on the people around me, nor is it allowing me to move outside of my comfort zone. Luckily, gameness is also contagious.

Now I look for the "most game" person in a situation and hook my wagon to theirs. More recently, the most game person in the room is me, and it's a refreshing role that I relish.

## PROCRASTINATION

Why on earth have humans evolved to have the ability to procrastinate? This mix of fear, laziness, sneakiness, and paralysis seems so unproductive and counter to survival that natural selection would have removed it dozens of generations ago. But no, it's flourishing. Everyone does it.

For me, procrastination is triggered by one of three things: being overwhelmed by the size of a task and not knowing where or how to start; being a perfectionist and not wanting to fail (which often means that even if I do manage to start something, I often don't finish it); or simply not liking the task. These triggers are common, as I've seen from some research. Unfortunately, the recommended solutions are at odds with the nature of procrastination: the steps experts suggest for overcoming procrastination are too complex for a procrastinator to even finish reading about.

Short of convincing myself that every task is life-threatening if I don't complete it and I ride an unsustainable wave of anxiety to get things done, I've found a more realistic solution in yoga: make it easy.

But the key here is: easy is not half-hearted. It's not "take it easy." To make something easy, there needs to be a strategy. This can mean start with something small: folding one pair of socks, washing one dish, or kneeling down on my yoga mat. That invariably leads to another sock, dish or posture– –I've started, after all, so I might as well do a bit more; it would be silly to only do that one, tiny thing.

Or, it can mean: find a way to simplify the task. In my yoga practice, my goal is to find a way to make the postures easy. Sometimes, this is a result of many hours of hard work until my brain figures out the right muscles to fire and which ones to relax. Practice ensures the required muscles are strong and flexible enough to perform when they need to. Once this happens, the posture—the task—is easier.

Sometimes, I find ease by not putting all of my effort into the posture—in a way, taking a lazy approach. But there's a strategy: the movement is still precise, just not full force, and the surprising result is usually just as effective a posture. It actually takes some effort to reduce my effort, because my default is mindlessly muscling through the posture, especially if it's familiar. To decrease the effort, I need to be more careful. The result is that I'm able to approach and tackle a posture on the mat, or a task off the mat, with a relaxed, attentive attitude, casting any fear, resistance, and procrastination aside.

Astonishingly, when the task is easy, the third procrastination trigger—dislike—goes away. Easy things tend to be fun because they're instantly gratifying.

I should note that tackling procrastination does not mean that I should barrel forward with all tasks at all times. There have been situations where I have waited—for example, before sending an email response in a conflict. During that pause, another development remedied the situation far more effectively than I would have with my email. But this is a risky strategy to rely on. I can pause to collect myself before doing something rash, but simply waiting to see what happens—

gambling—is no guarantee that I'll always get a lucky break.

**Procrastination and gambling can be a lethal combination.**

On a more complex level is the type of procrastination where I continue to do something. For example: not quitting a bad habit, like overeating, or spending a lot of time on my smartphone. Paradoxically, procrastination is about not doing something, so there is an opportunity to leverage a more fundamental facet of procrastination in the case of needing to stop: procrastinate on the bad habit. Just don't bother with more food. Don't bother staying on my phone. Do nothing. Be lazy about it. It can wait. It's an interesting paradigm shift that at times has worked for me. Perhaps this is where evolution has served humanity: we can also procrastinate on activities that can cause us harm—we avoid them.

I consider this: if there were not a term for procrastination, if it were not even considered a "thing", would I still be disabled by it? This is another approach to getting things done that I think has some merit. I don't think my grandfather was aware of procrastination. It was not part of his vocabulary, and he certainly didn't spend time researching, discussing, and thinking about the phenomenon. In other words, he didn't procrastinate by trying to understand procrastination. To someone struggling with it, he likely would have said, "Cut the shit. Just get it done." Sometimes that's what I have to do.

## DISCIPLINE

If I brush my teeth every day, then I can commit to a yoga practice.

I have a student who is struggling to make time to self-improve. She has two young kids, and she and her husband both work long hours. She has tried apps, scheduling software, and even electronic contraptions to help herself commit to yoga. Two other students want to prepay and schedule multiple sessions to commit. Another student literally asked me to "rake him over the coals" during the sessions as a way for him to feel that he was getting his money's worth and to justify the expense. In all cases, I've hesitated to comply. They're looking for reward or punishment as motivation. Neither are sustainable.

**Discipline is sustained and unemotional.**

And then I have another student who happens to be a body builder, and he asked for early morning sessions because he knows himself and that's when yoga suits him best. For me, that's the difference: leveraging my self-knowledge to create the best context for progress. People need to find and savor the aspect of their practice that resonates with them and use that as a way to keep coming back. This way, rewards and punishments don't factor into the equation.

**Progress on the yoga mat is the motivation.**

I was at a housewarming party in Los Angeles a while ago and got talking with an interesting woman about yoga. She had recently started private sessions three times a week. She loved the geometry of yoga and how she could learn about the relationship between each of the poses and how they affect different parts of her body, sometimes in unexpected ways. She said the one thing she was struggling with was trying to find a balance between self-acceptance and drive. How much should she practice? What is considered healthy? She didn't want to coddle herself, but she also didn't want to overdo it. She was wrestling with discipline.

She owns a very successful design company and has a dozen staff members. She's obviously driven and has managed to build an infrastructure that provides her and many other families with livelihoods. She said that for years she has existed "mostly in her head", and it's only now, at the age of fifty, that she has discovered the phenomenon of her body. She obviously thinks about things a great deal, hence her new fascination with how her body works, and how she is very much in control of her own fitness. She is not currently in a state of crisis and likely feels fine physically and mentally. There's no overt problem to solve on the mat, so her work is preventive and it's even more challenging to be disciplined: I feel fine—why should I work on wellness?

I suggested she consider replacing the idea of self-acceptance with self-awareness, which is more active and is not at odds with the concept of drive. The two work in tandem and will help her with discipline because the option of coddling or complacency is taken out of the equation. But it also guarantees that she won't go too far from what her body, brain, and life circumstances are equipped to handle. Self-acceptance without complacency is self-awareness.

For me, self-awareness is a deep, rational understanding of my limits, goals, and progress. It's the ongoing research I do to see where I am, what's holding me back, and how far I've come.

**Self-awareness and motivation work together beautifully as a goal-setting mechanism.**

## EQUANIMITY

It is a pleasure to see my students pause to regain their composure while standing on their mats during a particularly challenging sequence. Their faces are relaxed, and their breathing is even. They're covered in sweat, and they're exhausted, but they've learned the most effective way to find the energy they need to keep going is to be still, be patient with their discomfort, and let it dissolve. This is a delicate balance in a group that can be broken with one sigh, one step off the mat to pace through the fatigue, or one bend forward to rest hands on knees. In their stillness they're supporting each other as much as they're digging inward.

I think of this as equanimity. Any physical or mental sensations, any spikes or dips in their energy or mood, are equalized through this state of detachment. They don't slap their foreheads with frustration and pace circles around their mats, and they also don't laugh it off. They don't let the situation get the better of them and withdraw or act out. They just don't react. Their faces—telltale signs of emotion—are neutral. In most sessions I remind beginners to breathe and to keep their faces relaxed. This tends to neutralize emotions and to establish some stillness, which is a manifestation of equanimity. Their stillness is a type of focused relaxation. They're waiting and watching, with no endgame, no fight or flight response in waiting. They're safe, but alert.

I see equanimity in Olympians before a dive, a tumbling routine, or a ski race, and it's a challenging mental state to achieve. But it's not restricted to elite athletes. Anyone can muster it.

Firefighters, CEOs, chefs, and new parents can use equanimity to succeed in their tasks. Look at an in-control parent in a grocery store with a mid-tantrum child: cool as a cucumber.

On the mat, I'm mentally detached from the ups and downs of my physical state. This is part of my ongoing training. My emotional reaction to my physical self is a two-way street: I'm using my mind to calm my body to calm my mind.

Equanimity is not about being carefree. I care a great deal about myself, my friends and family, and my world. It's that I've learned from simple but intense experiences on the yoga mat that I can be most effective if I'm detached from the emotional highs and lows. If I can be mindful of my emotions, but not beholden to them, then they won't drive my decisions. I can experience the emotion—there's no way not to—but I don't anticipate it or dwell on it.

That being said, observing that emotion still helps me understand my interactions with the world; a useful function of emotion is empathy. My own emotional reactions, observed objectively, can help me understand why someone is behaving a certain way, especially if their emotions are influencing their own behavior, the very phenomenon I'm working to avoid.

I know all of this sounds like I'm suggesting that I deny myself the richness and texture of living, with all its bitterness and sweetness—basically acting like a Vulcan. No—it doesn't mean I appreciate the good things any less, or that I deny that bad things cause me pain, it just means I temper my emotional reactions to these spikes so that I can move on with a lightness and a sense of purpose.

**Emotions are like rain on a windshield while I'm driving. They blur my view and distract me from the task at hand.**

Even the tiniest spark of joy or curiosity from the buzz of receiving a text message on my phone is enough to throw me off track; my train of thought is interrupted, as are my focus and momentum. There are sounds all around me, but none distract me like my phone, and it's because there are emotions attached to it.

I had a laughing problem until fairly recently. It wasn't that I had trouble laughing; I often laughed when there was nothing funny happening, and I had trouble stopping. At a young age, when one of my parents was at the end of their rope with my brother's and my bickering, they brought their face close to ours and scolded us. The first thing that popped into my head was: don't laugh. This made me anxious, and of course, I started laughing. I'm laughing now as I write this, partly because in retrospect it's a funny thought, but mostly because I can very easily conjure that same feeling of anxiety that would cause the laughter. My parents must have thought I was either nuts or disrespectful, and their own irrational response set in—anger, anxiety, humiliation—making the situation worse.

This happened at school too, and it was contagious. I would start laughing at something trivial during a lecture—actually, it was more like shuddering because I was trying to stifle it—and a friend next to me would feel me shaking, look at my face, and they would start too. If the professor actually said something funny, we'd laugh more than the joke was worth just to open the steam valve a bit. This helped me calm down, and of course the teacher thought they were a comic genius.

This was not a nice feeling. I was not a happy-go-lucky kid who found humor in everything. I was a nervous wreck. I actually lived in fear that this nervous laughter would appear at the worst possible moments, as other people fear passing out in public or drawing a blank during a major corporate presentation.

This problem eventually vanished, seemingly by itself. But I know there's more to it. I'm older, for one thing, and I have a detachment, a distance, that allows me to separate my "self" from my emotions to gain some perspective. This has come in good part from yoga—a bit from the physical practice that requires me to not get flustered when I'm working through a more difficult posture, and a bit from the self-awareness that my yoga practice has allowed me to deepen.

For me, unwarranted laughter—if it could be called that—was a moderate psychological issue that I was dealing with. For others, it's stomach aches, migraines or lashing out, because of difficulty managing the emotions of uncomfortable situations. All emotional reactions, negative or positive, are indulgent; the roller-coaster nature of them—the high followed by the low—just doesn't feel good. Detachment from emotions— stepping back from them—allows me to observe those emotions more mindfully when they do happen and to reflect on the experience. When I'm standing still on my yoga mat, covered in sweat and working hard to maintain my composure and breath after a particularly challenging sequence, this is my proof of the value of this work. I ask myself: Why am I feeling this? What triggered this? What tools do I have to pull in the reins? So instead of having a mindless emotional response and stepping off my mat to escape, I'm—sometimes barely!—maintaining a level of equanimity: acknowledging the emotions but keeping them at arm's length.

## EXPECTATIONS

One way to foster equanimity is to manage expectations.

This does not mean having low expectations. Low expectations are a pre-emptive, negative outlook to prepare for a disappointing future, perhaps in an attempt to inoculate myself from pain. This can create a self-fulfilling prophesy; when my low expectations are met as planned, I'm still disappointed, although I suppose I do have the satisfaction of being right. The times when low expectations are exceeded are few and far between and are based on an unsustainable, broken dynamic.

Managing expectations really means having no expectations; applying equanimity to future events. In fact, I look to the future only for the necessities of planning. I thereby avoid the roller coaster of elation and disappointment, and instead experience an even-keeled acceptance of my current circumstances.

**The future will become the present soon enough without my constant, anxious speculation.**

Despite my best efforts to put expectations aside and not muscle through my yoga practice hell-bent on an anticipated result, sometimes I still find myself disappointed. But I've discovered a way to sidestep expectations: consider my practice an experiment. If I simply "see what happens" while I'm practicing, several good things happen: I'm more objective about my progress, I learn more about the process, and I often discover unanticipated, useful things about how my body and mind work.

Experimentation elevates my yoga practice from mindless repetition to mindful exploration. And since I'm basically using yoga to get better at living, this applies off the mat as well: cooking a meal, cleaning the house, having a conversation, working at a job. Experimentation keeps my day productive.

"Today, I'm going to master a handstand," in a no-expectation approach becomes, "Today, I'm going to practice my handstand using a couple of new techniques I've seen." It is constructive and confident, but not a cocky gamble. Off the mat, this can go from, "Today I'm going to march up to that contractor and get them to finish the renovation this week no matter what," to, "Today I'm going to discuss the progress with the contractor to determine how the renovation can be finished this week." This is no less assertive and much more rational. Of course, the contractor might not think the same way I do. But this is the reality of cultivating my own physical and mental transformation despite the nature of others. And it's still worth it.

Here, I need to remind myself that all of these experiences are part of the continuum of my and others' lives. This particular house renovation may take twice the amount of time promised, and the contractor may turn out to be awful. I learn from this experience, try to find recourse, and make sure that everyone's expectations are set more clearly or differently next time. Or, I can avoid this kind of interaction altogether in the future. Expectations will continue to go unmet during my lifetime. This is not giving up—it's having the wisdom to choose my battles.

**I have hopes and goals without expectations. I'm still optimistic, but my optimism stems from facts rather than emotions or entitlement.**

## MINDFULNESS

Mindfulness is confusing. It's a word that's used a lot now, and it seems to imply reflection and looking inward. In fact, it's the opposite. To be mindful is to focus my attention outward.

The truth is, I find the practice of mindfulness very challenging, so when I hear people throw the term around like it's as easy as flipping a switch, I don't believe them.

**For me, mindfulness is non-judgmental observation of my actions and surroundings.**

It's like waking up and experiencing my surroundings for the first time, without any preconceived notions or baggage. It's looking at the world with a relaxed focus.

Why is this important? By being non-judgmental, I'm removing emotions from my interactions with the world. In doing so, I'm getting "out of my head" and less likely to have my mind wander (which would usually be to negative thoughts, of course). By observing my actions and surroundings, I'm placing myself actively in the world and into the present moment.

Here's an example of a non-judgmental observation of my actions and surroundings:

I'm walking down the street, and I see a shoe. I notice the presence of the shoe in front of me: "There's a shoe." I notice its color and shape: "It's blue and white, and it has untied laces. It's also lying on its side, and I can see a worn sole."

That's it. This might sound obvious, and similar to what most of us do. But I'm convinced that we do not observe things quite so straightforwardly.

Here's an example of the opposite, and how my mind operates most of the time:

"There's a shoe! It's dirty and abandoned. I wonder whose it is? How could someone just drop a shoe like this? Oh—maybe they've had an accident. Should I do something? I hope this neighborhood isn't dangerous! I'm getting out of here!"

By allowing my mind to wander, I've caved to my emotions, and become indignant and then fearful for no rational reason. This is the mental equivalent to seeing an open bag of chips and eating the whole thing. I have indulged my urges.

Again, mindfulness is a challenging practice because I don't want to be bereft of emotion and empathy, like a robot, but I do want to be able to function rationally and productively in the world without the distraction of endlessly spinning thoughts.

Of course, I also don't want to deny myself the richness of the world and humanity: good food, laughter, sorrow. If I am mindful of these emotions, I'm free to experience them, savor them, but then I don't dwell on or anticipate them.

Here's another example:

I'm at the kitchen table. I have a bowl of raspberries in front of me. ("My mouth is watering.") I put a raspberry in my mouth and chew. ("I can smell the bowl of berries. They're fresh. The one I'm eating is sweet and juicy.") I swallow it and eat another one. ("I like these and I'm glad I have a bowl of them.")

I know this sounds a little forced, and if you met someone behaving this way with a bowl of raspberries, you might slowly back away. But consider the opposite: "I can't believe how expensive these raspberries were! They'd better be good. Ugh—there's one that looks squishy. Not gonna eat that one. Isn't there an e-coli outbreak or something right now? Damn, I forgot a spoon. Oh well. I'll just use my hands. I'm so hungry. Mmm! These are amazing! They're better than the frozen ones Sheila served at that dinner party. But everyone was so blitzed by the time we had dessert, nobody seemed to notice. I gotta stop drinking so much. Well, that didn't last long. I want more. What else have I got in the fridge?"

Here, I'm not enjoying the raspberries because I've allowed many more thoughts into my experience. I've muddied the waters and shortchanged myself.

The point here is that I'm focused on eating and enjoying the raspberries. The challenge is not to let emotions take over, because they will take me elsewhere—guaranteed!

The most effective way for me to spend some time being mindful, to slip into that calm awareness, is through breathing and movement. Yoga, in other words. Yoga postures' ever-increasing challenges keep my body and mind active, but not distracted. The built-in mindfulness of a yoga practice is now something I can start to conjure off the mat and apply to more than a bowl of raspberries.

**Yoga helps me cultivate mindfulness as a filter through which I can interact with the world in a productive, fulfilling, and calm way.**

This is the key, because even yoga can become repetitive and mindless. In retrospect, I think this is why I quit the hot yoga classes years ago. The poses were still challenging, but I knew the sequence and could make it through a class performing moderately well. As my fitness level increased, I could even start to coast a little, and this is where I started to think that maybe I didn't need it anymore. I now understand that the mindfulness required at the beginning, when it was still new to me, had all but disappeared, and I didn't have the motivation to continue. My body was getting stronger, and my mind was not keeping up with equal resilience.

So how did I re-ignite my commitment to yoga? A series of physical and mental crises, along with set of bittersweet but timely circumstances allowed me to pause and think about what my next career move was going to be. I wanted a new path that was sustainable health-wise. For me, understanding yoga as a practice, as opposed to a regimen, turned it into a source of limitless learning and variety. Teaching yoga turns my practice into a job, but it doesn't feel like work. The evidence of self-improvement while I practice or teach has made yoga very easy to commit to.

## A STUDIO

Given that yoga is an interplay between the external and the internal, it stands to reason that the space where I practice yoga is an important consideration.

For some, a yoga mat is all they need to create a practice space. They're able to extract themselves mentally from the distractions of their surroundings and focus their attention on the practice. For me, this is very challenging. My living space is a reflection of my mind. If that space is cluttered, then it's likely my yoga practice will be chaotic and ineffective.

I have noticed that the office and home spaces of others are an insight not just into their tastes, but into their mental states. As such, living spaces are very personal. Cluttered spaces and austere spaces can both send a message that I'm not welcome there. "Tuning in" to the space I live in and bringing order to it can get me a good way on the path to mental order as well. I've also been in spaces where I wanted to take a nap and stay forever. The spaces were neither cluttered nor stark, but struck a balance of meaningful objects, colors, and placement—a harmony, and not even necessarily in a "style" that I like—that seemed like a natural reflection of the warmth and stability of their owners.

Although my own yoga practice and the way I teach are quite earthbound, rational, and tangible, one of the few spiritual musts for me is that my yoga studio be a sacred space; stuff other than yoga does not happen in there. I've tried it other ways: hotel rooms, living rooms, outdoor patios—and it's been more challenging. I'm convinced it's because the spaces were not consecrated, so to speak. In other words, there was junk everywhere. How can I free myself from distraction if I willingly surround myself with it? Some yogis might argue that the practice of yoga is to train myself not to be susceptible to the distractions of my surroundings. Ideally, yes, but I would argue that if I can exert control over my environment, even a bit, that's the beginning of empowering myself in my practice, and it sets me up for success. There's nothing noble in torturing myself with visual and auditory clutter, especially if an uncluttered space will accelerate my learning and help to guarantee that my practice will be a long-term, stress-free endeavor.

I do not always have the luxury of a dedicated yoga space. Hence, the commercial yoga studio: I pay a certain amount, maybe some other people show up, and I've passed the job to someone else to make sure the space is free from distractions. When I attend a class in a studio, I get there a few minutes early to sit in and experience the space before others do, in effect consecrating it. By then I've already accomplished more on the yoga mat than I would have at home trying to practice behind the couch, distracted by my phone, my dog, or my husband. Distractions still exist in paid classes—the person next to me might be wearing sunglasses or jeans, drinking a latte, or muttering to themselves—all of which I have witnessed. The teacher and studio owners do have a responsibility to police distracting behavior for me to get the most for my money, but there's only so much they can do in exceptional circumstances. At this point they can still model behavior and teach this as an opportunity to build mental resilience, hopefully with a sidelong glance at the offenders!

During one of my many all-nighters in design school, I panicked. The model I was building was not coming together, and I was lost. Bits and pieces of material were strewn everywhere, my fingers were covered in glue and paint, and my stomach was sinking to my bowels. I was not going to make the deadline. It also didn't help that there was a grandfather clock in the house marking the loss of every half hour with a dramatic series of gongs. In an uncharacteristic fit of frustration, I swept everything off my worktable, ready to quit. Then, I paused because I started to feel the panic dissipate.

I was able to finish the project—by a hair—and everything worked out. My space had been cluttered and my brain foggy, partly from fatigue but also from the physical chaos around me. Clearing off the table was a reset that had an immediate effect. Since then, I've done this many times when I've felt confused or anxious doing office work, studying, or sorting out a crisis. Now, carefully and methodically—not dramatically—I clean up my physical surroundings. The process of tidying up—the ritual itself—is an integral part of clearing my head. I suspect if I snapped my fingers (or hired someone) and the space was suddenly clean, the impact on my mind would not be quite the same.

Like me, the space I practice in will never be perfect. But in looking to achieve some sacredness, it must be treated with respect and reverence. My surroundings can support me, and they can distract me. My challenge is to savor the natural light, the simplicity, the clean floor, the white walls, and to gracefully accept and let fall to the background the cracks in the concrete, the flies that buzz around when the door is open, the sound of the leaf blowers, and the traffic outside.

Each time I practice yoga, I create a clean mental slate. I roll out the mat, put my phone away, close the door, and begin. This is a small ritual, and it triggers a big change in my mind. I'm not religious, but I imagine shrines, altars, and prayer create a comparable mental state for some people. The difference in yoga is that in carefully creating a sacred space for myself, I'm in effect consecrating myself.

**I become the sacred object within my practice space, with a deep reverence for the wonders of what my body and mind can do.**

## PLEASURE

For most of my adult life, I viewed pleasure as indulgence. Accordingly, there was guilt, confusion, and a whole lot of baggage associated with allowing myself to seek and experience pleasure. I believed that everyone eventually pays for pleasure (a hangover, a stomachache, a sunburn), or that its pursuit was only possible to the detriment of those around me (a good laugh at someone else's expense). Pleasure to me was wicked. But I still indulged in what I saw as pleasurable activities because they seemed to feel good, and I felt entitled. Of course, the result was often messy.

By definition, pleasure, or a pleasant thing, gives me a sense of happy satisfaction. I like the way this sounds because it seems light and innocent. But it's at odds with what I saw as pleasurable activities: drinking a martini, eating rich cheese, watching a horror movie. Maybe one bite, one sip, or one scene is momentarily sensorial or thrilling, but of course it never stops with just one.

The problem was that I had not stopped to think about the organic nature of pleasure and of its pursuit. The fact is, it can sour. It depends on the amount and, more importantly, what I deem pleasurable. Watching twelve hours of slapstick comedy probably stops being pleasant, even if I'm laughing the whole time—in fact, especially if I'm laughing the whole time. One of my teachers once pointed out that even a purely pleasurable thing, like a massage, can become unpleasant if experienced for too long, too often, or under the wrong circumstances.

For a long time, the things I saw as unpleasant were exercise, salad, and, literally, moderation. When someone claimed a jog outside was pleasant, I didn't believe them. Nor did I believe they could find pleasure in moderating their intake of anything. Pleasure was supposed to be going all the way! Being free and letting go! Living it up! I did not see pleasure as a quiet sense of satisfaction.

When we lived in Boston, an evening with friends started with martinis, and then progressed to multiple bottles of wine, a big meal, and a rich dessert. (I'm not blaming Boston—it's all on me.) It seemed that it was only possible to have a good time via these indulgences, and I accepted any illness the next day as an unavoidable side effect of "feeling good" during a fun evening with friends. I worked hard to find affirmation that indulgences were actually healthy to justify them: cheese has calcium! Alcohol can be good for my heart! Horror movies are an escape! And the internet offers up these theories, justifications, and permissions by the thousands.

Then, during my heart surgery recovery, I went through a period where I did not experience these indulgences; they would have conflicted with the blood thinners and other medications. I gained several months of distance from them, enough to slowly start to ask myself: are these things pleasant? Do they give me a happy sense of satisfaction? No. I had confused pleasure from these indulgences with the pleasure of getting together with friends. I realized they are not mutually dependent. I got over the awkwardness I felt when I was the only one not drinking and realized I didn't need it to have a nice time. In fact, I started to understand that even while indulging, I actually used to feel physically and mentally ill. It was subtle, but it was there: haziness, nausea, line-crossing humor, and every time, regret. Leading up to our wedding, a good friend gave me the best advice for the day: "Don't get drunk. You'll miss a lot of amazing things." It was tempting, given others' revelry, but I deeply appreciate being able to look back on and savor every wonderful detail of the event.

Indulgence aside, I struggle with whether it's useful to have an expectation that everything I do, including the pursuit of wellness, be pleasurable for the entire duration of that activity. I suspect if I clung to that hope, I'd stop all activities altogether. There are always bumps in the road: they're what make me resilient.

**Practicing yoga has given me a clearer view of "before and after" and "cause and effect", which has altered my perception of pleasure.**

My practice, which is an ongoing experiment, invariably leaves me feeling better afterwards than before, even if at some point during the practice I feel tired, sore, or frustrated. I consistently feel worse after a martini than before, even if at some point while drinking it I feel elated. This awareness of my body's and my mind's reactions to activities has helped me to become vegan, to stop drinking, and to sustain those decisions. There is pleasure in abstinence—a sense of longing, of missing out can be pleasurable in that it's a sensation, like all others, that helps me understand my urges and how fleeting they really are. Two minutes after deciding not to accept a drink renders a pleasurable sense of accomplishment, and the raised awareness is revelatory. This sensation is a new addition to my ever-expanding understanding of what can be pleasurable.

Of course, I don't live in a bubble insulated from the indulgences that I used to act on, especially if they're paired with getting together with close friends. But yoga has zoomed me in to a more subtle, nuanced sense of pleasure, and I no longer seek heightened sensual experiences to feel satisfied. These were moving targets that required an ever-increasing intensity for the next one to match the last.

**A late-night rager is not pleasant; it's a destabilizing loss of inhibition.**

Admittedly, I've learned to be careful on the yoga mat as well. It's possible to lose control in the pursuit of thrilling postures in yoga, and this can lead to injuries and make me feel worse than when I started. But some sweat, a deep stretch, and a few moments of sitting silently does feel good now. Off the mat, having a nice conversation with a trusted friend, or a long meal with a group of fun-loving acquaintances makes me happy. These are real pleasures, and they are always achievable and sustainable.

## PATIENCE

When I become impatient, it's because my expectations of timing have not been met. If this is repeated, frustration sets in. For example, if I'm working to achieve a handstand or an arm balance by a certain deadline, I'm setting myself up for disappointment and a sense of underachievement, neither of which are conducive to progress. Goals are useful, but unless I'm competing professionally, it's foolish for them to be fixed to the passage of time.

**The goal of my yoga practice is the practice itself.**

When my expectations are not driven by time, urgency is removed and the accomplishment, when it does happen, invariably feels like it happened sooner than I was expecting.

Patience is by no means complacency. Actually, it takes more effort to remain patient outside of time constraints because there's no opportunity to give up. I see patience as a kind of faith.

**Patience is sustained trust, freed from the constraints of time.**

Off the mat, the difference is that outsiders are part of the equation: waiting for accountants to complete our tax filing, waiting for a contractor to finish a renovation to my house, waiting for my spouse to finish up in the bathroom, waiting for a friend to meet me at a café. These are all situations where there is not an unlimited amount of time. But I have realized something that is embarrassingly obvious: becoming impatient (disappointed, angry, accusatory, frustrated…take your pick) does not accelerate a result. If anything, impatience really messes with my perception of the passage of time and makes it seem to take longer.

I often have to ask myself, "where is this impatience coming from?" My adult circumstances have evidently made me less patient. A useful analogy is untangling a rope. This is a frustrating task, but I've learned over time that panicking and rushing to untangle it furiously will lead to more frustration. I need to stop, look, find the end and methodically untangle it. I know how to do this. I was incredibly patient as a kid. I'd sit down, get comfy, and show my parents how it's done. I had all the time in the world, and I've come to see that my adult perception of time is what frustrates me when I'm struggling with a task.

I've been taught to be impatient, as if it's a virtue. I still feel a spike of anxiety at an intersection when the light turns green because I expect a Boston driver behind me to honk after a millisecond, even though I live in a small town in California where drivers never use their horns. An efficient person needs to be impatient, right? Wrong. Impatience is focused entirely on the destination at the expense of savoring, strengthening, and learning from all the points along the way. I guarantee that a patient person outperforms an impatient one ninety-nine percent of the time. And the remaining one percent: impatient people may win, but it's at the expense of their health and that of everyone around them.

One of my students recently left his high-paying, high-stress job. Literally within a week of quitting, he was a different person on the yoga mat. Yoga had been stressful for him. He would often ask how he was doing, or how much time was left, and he always brought to the studio an enormous iced coffee, which made him jittery. His urgency to perform, his focus on results and on the end of the session was making me nervous, not to mention turning him into a wreck. I suspect he returned weekly not because he saw positive results and wanted to build on them, but because he was hell-bent on achieving a goal that he had set for himself, or that someone had set for him.

When his job ended, a switch flipped. He stopped bringing coffee into the studio, maybe because he was getting more sleep. The sessions went by quickly for him and for me, and he had a handful of physical breakthroughs. This might seem like an unusual case where a change in someone's outside life enables an improvement on the mat. But, arguably, had he not been practicing yoga in the first place, he might not have left his job. The firsthand struggles he had on the yoga mat might have been an upsetting reality that forced him to face his health and his mindset, both of which were difficult to measure in any other way. It's possible he was bringing his work identity to his yoga practice, and when his job ended, he felt unburdened and allowed his truer self to show. This is a useful proof that yoga is not a bubble; his behavior on the yoga mat might have helped provide the evidence that he needed to make a change. He has since taken another stressful job, but hopefully this exposure to another way of feeling and interacting with the world has given him tools to cope with the realities off the mat.

## Patience is a discipline to preserve my well-being.

I have tools: breathing and mindfulness. My breathing is connected to my sense of time, and therefore to my patience. While driving in a panic through heavy traffic to get to a new client meeting, I once had this insight: "fuck it. This is out of my control." I let out a deep sigh of resignation and simply paid attention to driving. Ten minutes later I arrived at the meeting on time. I would have arrived at the same time whether I was relaxed or not, but relaxing slowed my perception of the passage of time. I burned less energy worrying and breezed into the meeting meadow-fresh.

When I teach, I encourage students to mark the passage of time with breathing. I'm so familiar with the use of minutes that I can gauge pretty accurately what time of day it is—usually within five minutes—without looking at a clock. This is a useful skill for sticking to a schedule, but it is unnatural. When students start to count their breaths, invariably the breathing slows and they calm down, even if they're in a strenuous posture. They're being patient with their circumstances, and in turn patient with themselves, which is transformative. After all, what's the rush?

To be patient is to focus on where I am in my journey. Transformation does not happen in one fell swoop at the destination; it's a series of discoveries along the way. Every moment I wait patiently, not idle but breathing and mindful, is an opportunity to learn one more tiny piece about the task at hand, and about myself.

# LEARNING

When I'm teaching others, I'm learning too. For years I did not see that these things are inseparable. I know I'm continuously learning; I didn't realize I'm continuously teaching. I model behavior, for better or worse: with kids, colleagues, my spouse, even with someone I meet on the street. By doing that, I reveal something about myself. There's an exchange that's impossible to prevent. Even if it's my nature not to "let on", then that's what I'm teaching.

I've attended high school. I've attended university. I've spent a weekend learning to bake bread. The courses were designed so that I could be exposed to a new skill, and then apply what I learned on my own. Which I did, temporarily. Then most of what I learned faded. Had I learned anything? I had absorbed enough to recall it to pass exams, but as it turns out, that's it.

Years ago, I didn't realize that the training I had completed was to just get me started. Real learning, the stuff that sticks, occurs in practice.

The same is true for yoga. Given that I firmly believe that yoga must be a lifelong endeavor, there must be real learning, through practice, to progress. Physical and mental fitness are not sustainable without learning. I approach my practice that way: I look at every session as an opportunity to gain even a tiny addition to my understanding of how my mind and body work, or don't work.

**Every time I'm on the yoga mat,
I learn something new.**

When I decided to take my first of several in-depth yoga teacher training courses, my biggest fear was whether I'd still be able to learn something new. Leading up to my yoga training, I had not thought about learning for decades. Of course, I had still been learning—as an employee, an employer, a boyfriend, a husband, a dog owner...but these were all indirect forms of learning that were driven by necessity. Rarely did I actively assimilate new information like I tried to back in school. I suppose I thought those days were thankfully behind me. Learning and exams were stressful, and I accepted them as a necessary rite of passage and not something I'd continue to endure.

In school, I teetered on the edge of an undisciplined way of learning. I rarely asked myself why the information was important and how I could observe and manipulate it from different angles. Emboldened by high grades I was often cocky and reviewed the material mindlessly. Periodically, to my surprise, I froze on exam questions when I couldn't immediately regurgitate an answer. Then, I'd get a floating feeling, almost like I was about to drift up and over my desk.

I understand now this was my blood pressure spiking. Sometimes I could save myself by "figuring it out" on the spot: literally piecing together bits of knowledge to teach myself how to complete an equation or answer an essay question. This felt like a victory, but it also felt horrible. An ignorance of how to learn kept me in this cycle of elevated anxiety.

So when I started my yoga career, I didn't know if or how I could apply my old way of learning to this new field, let alone teach it. I was nervous about this cycle starting again, but I was fine. Yes, there was theory, terminology, language, and sequencing that was important to know, but this was background for the practical aspects of yoga that I was learning by doing.

Here's what I experienced: I got on the mat. I was bombarded with information, and my mind's miraculous way of re-wiring itself took care of the learning for me. I was confused and overwhelmed at times. This was good! I savored the richness of the stream. I slept on it. I relaxed with it. I kept at it.

I slowly gained the ability to apply this way of mind-body learning to other aspects of my life, with my yoga practice as the model. I look with excitement at what seems like impenetrable gibberish in my life that will soon become second nature.

That floating anxiety rarely happens to me now, mostly because of yoga. I've learned how to learn. My interests and needs shift as I get older. I'm still driven, but I simply don't care if I fail at some things. In the past I was hellbent on succeeding at everything. My process for learning—small chunks, practice, and patience—is very personal, as is my discretion for what I choose to learn and excel at. I've identified and refined my approach to learning, thanks to my yoga practice.

When I don't know what I'm doing, I eagerly admit it. I know that even if I can fake it for a time, my ineptitude will catch up to me. This is true for the best of fakers, and I know this because I used to be one. Now, when I'm facing a deadline or a test (and this comes in many forms), I channel the vibe from the yoga mat—relaxed breathing, vulnerability, equanimity, absorption and access—and it works. Success, or progress, is no longer achieved by the seat of my pants, nor is it a fluke: it's the result of honesty, and it's truly earned.

## COMMUNICATION

Teaching is communicating. I communicate an idea to my students, and they communicate a response. I might be clear enough for them to "get it" and execute the posture, or they might fumble, hesitate, or look around, confused. They might have zoned out (perhaps because I was momentarily not entertaining enough to hold their interest) and are stumbling to catch up. All of this tells me something about this exchange.

Where was the lapse in communication? Was it between me and the student, or was it internal to the student? Did their brain absorb and process the instruction, but then the transition to a physical movement was a much less familiar set of commands, most of which they're only starting to get comfortable with? Many sequences of movement—in dance, yoga, or football—can look easy from the outside but give me a false sense of confidence that is shattered when that movement is put into practice. I only see the polished end result on YouTube. My mind tells my body things, and my body sends messages to my brain. Everything is absorbed, interpreted, regurgitated, and yes, miscommunicated.

**An impasse, or conflict, is almost always possible to resolve. This idea must be the starting point of all discussions.**

If clear, rational discussion does not result in a constructive step forward, then it's likely one or both sides lack the tools, or possibly the willingness, to reach an understanding, consciously or not.

No two monsters speak the same language, which is never the language of balanced, thoughtful human beings. That's why monsters create such unpleasant circumstances.

The immediacy of a yoga session's call and response format—I say raise an arm, and someone raises an arm—has been a humbling way to face and evaluate my teaching and therefore my communication skills. This is far more evident than in a more conventional teaching format: speak or demonstrate, assume it's being absorbed by the students, and then weeks later test them. In yoga, the students (and I!) are tested at the same time as the instruction. It's the ultimate form of active learning. There are the spoken words and actions, and then there are the more subtle messages being communicated both ways: fatigue, frustration, distraction, disinterest. I need to tune in to those to keep the session moving to a satisfactory conclusion.

Yoga brings communication, internal and external, subtle and explicit, to the forefront. It shows me that I am always partly responsible for every moment of clarity and every lapse, and that through practice my communication skills can improve.

## WORDS

Words can be the most clear and rational way to communicate an idea, but they can also be the most misleading, inefficient, and harmful. Sometimes I grow complacent in my word choices, and I have to stop and remind myself:

**If I will not say something to a stranger, I must not say it to a loved one.**

And it's the same in reverse. This is particularly important for words that cause harm. Everyone has that friend who's unpleasant to waitstaff. Everyone knows a couple who are cordial to friends, but painfully rude to each other. Is it intentional or simply careless?

Yoga, and especially teaching, has made me a better listener and also reminded me that people are listening to me; my words have an impact on people. I never really gave that much thought. I do filter what I say to children to make sure that it is clear and focused, considering the impact, yet I assume a much greater resilience when it comes to adults. Why not give the same care to my words in grown-up conversations? Do I stand to lose meaning or impact? With clarity—saying what I really mean—comes a certain amount of vulnerability. Maybe I'm comfortable showing that to kids, but with my peers I'm more guarded, and therefore possibly vaguer, and even unintentionally harmful. They deserve more respect.

I often see a disconnect between the words yoga teachers use in class and how they handle themselves in their day-to-day activities. Maybe this is okay; after all, they're just doing their job and they're being paid for wise words and guidance. I see this in politicians and other authority figures daily. My high school chemistry teacher likely did not spend his evenings playing with uranium after describing its half-life in a lecture. But it does make me wary; I once received an angry, knee-jerk email from a disgruntled yoga studio owner over a scheduling problem, and yet the email signature still said, "sending love and light." This made me chuckle. When words and actions don't match, then the speaker might not actually understand what they're saying, or they don't believe it themselves. I steer clear of a personal trainer I see smoking outside the gym.

### Words can set tone.

When I'm teaching, I'm a guide. I'm making suggestions not just for the small adjustments the students can make to benefit more fully from the postures, but for the practice as a whole. At the same time, I'm considering why I'm saying certain things: is it to help them or me? It was easy early on as a teacher to bark out commands that were to be followed. I've softened since then. It's not that I'm coddling the students as per the cliché of wellness practices, I'm empowering the students to make the movements of their own volition. My earlier aggression was a reflection of my insecurity. I felt that if I didn't make the class strict, they would not fall in line and perform to their full potential. They'd get disappointed with themselves and me, and they wouldn't come back. Now, I tune into the ebb and flow of the session: sometimes firmness is needed, at other times some comfort gets them to their potential. "Bend your forward knee more!" has become, "You can bend your forward knee more deeply into the lunge."

Just the addition of "you can" has the dual effect of saying, "I know you can do this" and "It's up to you." Ninety-five percent of the time, they bend that knee more, and the other five percent of the time, there's usually a good reason that they don't, like an injury or fatigue. They let me know why they can't, and this approach keeps the dynamic agreeable, two-sided, and progressive. Listening is as much a part of my teaching as talking.

In the seemingly simple context of a yoga session, this careful consideration of the impact of words on progress has taught me a great deal about my interactions off the mat. Here are some other examples:

### I try to avoid using would, should, and could.

These are vague, lazy, and therefore dangerous words. They camouflage my intention and allow me to dole out advice without committing to why. But if I take them out of a phrase like, "You should try this sandwich," it might become, "I want you to taste this sandwich because it will broaden your palate." That's a bit arrogant for a conversation about a sandwich. How do I know their palate will broaden? Digging a little deeper into why I really want them to try that sandwich, I say it in a more personal, vulnerable way, like this: "I'm enjoying this sandwich and I want you to enjoy it too. Have some." Yes, this takes hard work, and it's a little awkward. But it's also clearer and intentional, and there's no risk of a misunderstanding or of misplaced intentions. It's a challenging exercise to avoid would, should, and could, but it gets easier, and it's worth the effort.

## Sarcasm is poisonous.

Even the tiniest bit of sarcasm, intended as a joke, chips away at a relationship and is guaranteed to have negative consequences. How could saying the opposite of what's right—the opposite of what I mean—ever help a topic progress or improve a dynamic? My husband once had a staff designer who did good work, but he mostly spoke sarcastically. He might have thought his tone was a hip, funny cynicism, or it's more likely he felt insecure. Unfortunately, over time, his interactions with colleagues left them baffled and often hurt. Everything was misunderstood, and despite his talent, he was eventually fired. The powerful takeaway was that nobody identified that his primary problem was sarcasm. There were evidently deeper issues at hand, but had he been forced to address his choice of words at any point, it might have triggered a tiny change in him that could have grown to have a positive impact on his interactions and possibly entire outlook.

Similarly, poking fun at someone gradually wears thin, despite the childhood myth that it's a sign of affection. I like attention, but clearly, a compliment is more nurturing than an insult.

My brother, as an adult, continued to get together with his childhood male friends. They all had a habit of 'jabs': supposedly innocent insults to each other's skills, accomplishments, or relationships. Eventually, my brother started to dread getting together with them—it was impossible to put a steak on a barbeque without a joke about ineptitude. He knew they all cared for each other and their history ran deep, but the words still mattered.

He tried to model better behavior for them, but it fell on deaf ears, and so for a couple of years he stopped seeing them as a group, although he still enjoyed seeing them individually. A shared history was not enough to shield him from the constant, "playful" barrage of insults. An insult usually stems from the insecurity of the speaker and their discomfort with showing kindness or fondness, which are perhaps seen as weak. Several of my uncles were this way with their kids, particularly their sons. This oddly competitive dynamic sadly resulted mostly in missed opportunities for bonding and empowerment.

I've learned my own lesson several times as a yoga teacher when, amid self-deprecating laughter about someone falling out of a posture, it seemed right to throw in a joke. It was not. I don't know how someone will internalize my words and lose trust. I can make fun of myself to put people at ease, but not of someone else.

### I always speak affirmatively and constructively.

When I teach yoga, if a student's left leg is obviously weaker or less flexible than their right one, I don't say, "your left leg is weak; we have lots of work to do" because I have found this is deflating. It's honest, but I can take more care with my honesty, and state it affirmatively and constructively: "Your right leg is stronger. Let's work to have the left leg catch up!" —same goal, very different approach.

It's generally accepted that talk therapy works. Verbalizing a problem forces me to not only face it, but the work of articulating that problem helps me to rationalize it. Very often by the time I've finished describing a struggle to someone, I'm partway to figuring out a solution. But this cannot be accomplished without practice, honesty, and a genuine will to find a solution. What if the listener is very biased? What if everything I'm saying is biased and poisonous? Does that help me or make it worse, possibly even affecting the listener in a negative way? Even worse is repeating the same poison over and over again, like a mantra, with nobody willing to help stop the negative cycle. I'm reinforcing the problem rather than coming up with a solution and slowly chipping away at the resilience of those around me. There is a fine line between talking to reinforce a problem and talking to solve it. All of this takes work on my part, and on the part of the listener. It's a type of training, like yoga, and it gets easier.

The most impactful conversation I've had with a friend was years ago, during a deep emotional and financial crisis. Our business was on the edge of collapse, and I was anxious and depressed from the moment I woke up every morning. I spent a few minutes unloading to this friend, who also shared office space with us. At the end of my rant, all he said was, "That sounds awful. What are you going to do?" I was stunned at first. This was not the response I was after. But it was the best thing he could have said. He acknowledged the direness of my situation, and then reminded me that he knew I could fix it. It was a tremendously empowering, yet tiny push.

I've worked hard in the past decade to extract myself from misery-company dynamics. I only share problems with people equipped to listen and help me come up with solutions, and I reciprocate when they need me. I've learned that at times, depending on circumstances and company, saying nothing is best. At other times, my sunny outlook and rational problem solving feels awkward, forced, and kooky. But that's partly because I'm culturally trained to see things as worse than they actually are: cynically viewing the world as bleak, aggressive, joyless, and doomed. But this is no more "real" than looking at the world through rose-colored glasses. Ultimately, I strive for an even-keeled outlook: not one caked in mud nor in glitter, but somewhere in between.

**I strive to only say things that benefit me and my listener.**

This is one of the more challenging ways of having a conversation. How do I know if it will benefit them? Well, it's mostly about my intention. When I think of it that way, is it really so hard? Why would I say something of no benefit to the other person? There is value in economy of words and thoughtful content. Some people may love the exercise (introverts), while others may hate it (extroverts).

"The weather is beautiful today." Does this benefit me to say? Possibly as a daily affirmation, but arguably no. Does this benefit the listener? If they're standing in front of me, then they likely already think the weather is beautiful.

"I've been depressed lately, and this beautiful weather has raised my mood." This benefits me because I'm reflecting and committing to the idea that I can improve my mood. This might also benefit the listener because it's a morsel of personal insight and vulnerability that might also help them manage their mood, and sharing this will strengthen our bond.

As a teacher, I have to be very careful with the words I choose. The same instruction can be given to two people, and they'll do very different things. But yoga is two-sided, just like any other dynamic, and the responsibility lies with the teacher and the student to make sure that the intent matches the action. When teaching, I'm careful not to demonstrate postures unless absolutely necessary, but to describe them instead. I also don't name the postures, except with more advanced students. This benefits me, because it strengthens my communication skills, but it also benefits the student: they have to stay present, listen carefully, and not 'anticipate the green light' by rushing from one posture to the next. They also don't bring their own preconceived notions or baggage associated with the postures to the mat. I consciously use the session as a way to free them from old patterns of behavior—reactions to words—so that every session is a series of active discoveries. This invariably makes its way off the mat, and brings an openness, precision, and honesty to daily interactions.

By making sure that everything I say is truthful, meaningful, and does not cause harm, I'm strengthening the bond I have with loved ones and affirming our mutual value. And I'm getting the job done effectively: I'm saying what I mean, and people understand me.

I always have an intention, an impulse, a will brewing inside me, and my words deserve careful consideration to ensure that this intention is conveyed in the best possible way.

## A CLASS

A class is a dialogue between a teacher and students dedicated to arriving at a shared understanding of a particular topic. A yoga class is an opportunity, unlike any other, for an increased understanding of the self.

The economics of mainstream yoga don't allow for it to be taught as intended. Originally, yoga was one-on-one: a student and a teacher. Now, a class can be filled to capacity, and some sessions more of an event than a practice. Dozens of students wait giddily for the teacher to appear, a few welcome words are spoken, and the class begins. Here and there the teacher, or their assistants, make adjustments to as many students as time will allow, and then the class ends with many of the attendees leaving without a word to the teacher or to each other. This is what enables yoga teachers to make a living, partly because a gym-culture population doesn't believe that any fitness class should cost more than ten dollars. Everyone still learns something, but deep learning from individualized attention cannot happen as easily with large classes. The teacher and students miss out on valuable insights.

When I used to teach at large studios, sometimes there would only be two or three people in the class. I slowly started to appreciate something that at first was awkward and a bit humiliating: doesn't anyone like my classes?!? Small groups were more personal. I felt like I was more helpful, and overall the sessions were less one-sided and more fun. I couldn't hide behind my dialogue and blindly bark out instructions in the hopes that most of the group would understand, and the few students there certainly couldn't hide behind each other. We had no choice but to connect fully. In large classes, I would get a horrible feeling when a student struggled with a posture, and circumstances of time and crowding prevented me from helping them. It was like watching someone drown and not throwing them a rope, all the while hoping absurdly that they'll come back for another swimming lesson!

So at one point I made the decision to shift to appointment-based private yoga, like a personal trainer. My sessions allow a maximum of four people, which was originally a space restriction: the studio can only fit four people. But I quickly realized the restriction has some merit: four is the maximum number of people that I still feel I can deliver the attention to and give them the value for their money. Thanks, universe!

The good thing about this format is that I get to try some new things. I get to know the students really well. I can track their improvement more closely, and so can they. And I always remind them how far they've come.

I sometimes miss the energy and camaraderie of large classes—there is something inspiring about a group of people working hard, together but alone, through their mental and physical limitations. There's a quiet, unspoken atmosphere of support. Sometimes, it's important for my individual students to experience this. Vulnerability in a semi-public setting is another pathway to resilience, especially when a struggle is shared.

I struggle with my own ideas of what things should cost. How much will I pay for a glass of wine or a meal? How much for a pair of jeans? How much for a suit to wear to a wedding? Does the benefit outweigh the cost for any of these things? Yoga is indeed an abstract activity, but it has such tangible results that it has helped me shuffle my priorities for what I'm willing to spend money on and what I'm not.

**Yoga has options: I can spend as much or as little money as I want, and I can practice on my own or in a group.**

In the interest of profit, yoga has been elevated in many places to feel exclusive: high-end studios, clothing, and equipment, and it's therefore seen as a luxury—unnecessary or inaccessible. When people are tight on cash, yoga is often the first to go, which is unfortunate because its absence—missing its therapeutic benefits—can create quite a void. But even in the handful of times I've had students stop sessions with me because of money, I've reminded them that yoga couldn't be more accessible, more for everyone and that they can find a way to keep practicing on their own. Technically, yoga is free. Nobody holds a license or patent— though some have tried. The proof is online and in books. Everyone is trying things and showing people. The industry is rich and full of options for them to continue.

A yoga practice is an organic, enriching, personal pursuit. A yoga class, whether it's in a big or small group, reminds me of the shared experience of humanity. In any form and place, it's a familiar anchor that I can always rely on to clarify what I truly value. I just need to figure out what format will allow me to learn the most and encourage myself to keep at it, knowing that my circumstances are constantly in flux.

## A STUDENT

My students are an invaluable way for me to gain insights into the human condition. Their motivation to get onto the mat and the obstacles they encounter when practicing, all of which are generated from within themselves, are fascinating reflections of our humanity. I'm grateful for the access to this wealth of insight and for their willingness to open themselves to this exchange.

And despite the contemporary image of a yoga practitioner as lean, young, flexible, pony-tailed, all-knowing, good-smelling, detoxified, and light-footed, my students run the gamut.

A few years ago, one of my students experienced what he called a widow-maker: a sudden, severe heart attack that brought him to the brink of death. He lost consciousness while riding the subway in his hometown. He was resuscitated by fellow passengers and woke up two weeks later in a hospital room unaware of what had happened, somehow breaking his leg. He did not lead an unhealthy lifestyle at the time, except for stress. He's in his seventies now, and his yoga practice is smooth and consistent. He's unflappable, quiet, and determined when we meet.

Another of my students, who happens to be my husband Duane, suffers from monthlong bouts of migraines every three or four years. He has had every test imaginable to determine the source, and the most frequent diagnosis is that they're brought on by stress. Yet, he says he does not feel stressed. He's working as an architect (a childhood dream of his he only started to pursue at the age of forty-five), he has a loving home and husband (me!), and a solid network of friends. However, his most recent attack happened after a handful of tragedies: his father had died, his brother had died, and his mother had had cancer and a mastectomy. He had also been confronted about the legitimacy of his new career by an authority figure who felt that in light of his success and renown, he had not paid his dues. All of this, Duane realized, was unaddressed grief and indeed a type of stress. Duane uses the studio now to meditate. And he generously gives me his time to try out new sequences on him!

I have worked with a business owner who told me several times how much he hates yoga. To him, it is a necessary evil for curing debilitating sciatica. After a handful of sessions the pain and numbness dissolved, and yet he kept coming for sessions as a preventive measure. He felt better but did not seem to be enjoying yoga. He swore, groaned, and frowned with every move. I lightheartedly suggested he not torture himself to this degree, that there was a way to find comfort in each posture, and he'd glare at me as if I was suggesting he levitate. His stubbornness showed in his lack of physical flexibility and open frustration with some of the postures. It was a challenge for me to have him in the studio, and I started to share his disdain for our meetings. There was a lapse in our communication that I was not able to overcome before he finally stopped practicing with me. I don't regret that this happened, but I do look forward to another chance, maybe with someone else, to address similar attitudes.

And I also work with his opposite. For six months of each year, while he's in town, an artist comes to my studio to practice. Every minute of the session is a revelation to him and an opportunity to learn more about himself. I struggle to keep up with him! He's joyful, present, and contemplative. Even during challenging postures he's able to maintain an equanimity that is amazing: rather than groan into a deep stretch, he simply says, "Okay, that's a little uncomfortable," and keeps at it.

Although I have not brought it up with her, vulnerability is an aspect of another student's personality that she is unwilling to show. She's smart and socially connected. She manages a team of people and is very much embedded in a corporate lifestyle. Perhaps because of her office dynamic, she does not allow any cracks to show. On the yoga mat, she understands the postures and the benefits, including the psychological ones, and yet over the course of a few months, she progressed very little in her practice. She reminds me repeatedly of her physical limitations, and she is unwilling to take even the smallest risk, not because there is a danger of injury, but I suspect because there is a risk of failure. I hope that sometime soon she will identify and share her fears with me; I know that merely in doing so, she will succeed in pushing past them.

At the end of some sessions, I'll ask people for their thoughts. Some people see this as fishing for compliments on how well I put together the sequences. It's not, though! I want them to introspect and consider the biggest takeaway from the session—what they've learned—and share it. There's an exchange that helps both of us; it keeps them vigilant and actively learning if they have to say something about it, and it always provides useful insights for me to confirm if what I thought I was conveying was actually what they picked up.

So what is a good student? In retrospect, I don't think I was a good student back in school. I was a good mimic. The lack of capacity to think broadly was in part due to my age, in part to flaws in the education system, and in part due to my own stubbornness and fear of failure: they told me to do it this way, so why risk losing a grade by trying something else? I didn't want to experiment because I didn't want to risk a miss.

**I've realized learning is about self-actualization, not fitting into a role.**

From the people who come to my studio, and from my own ongoing training, I've learned that a good student is someone who trusts themselves, who is honest and game, and who communicates well. They are able to see the interconnectedness of all of their life and work activities, including yoga. And specifically to yoga, they understand that sometimes they need to move their attention away from their head to the rest of their body. For some, the work on the yoga mat is for them to become a good student. For others, it's a matter of overcoming self-imposed limitations to put into practice what they've so effectively learned.

## A TEACHER

Teacher, mentor, guide, coach—whatever the most appropriate word—is an oddly exhausting service. People pay me to make them work, not to do the work for them. And that takes a lot of work!

My yoga training was the first time I'd seen a teacher as a guide, although I now realize I've had many guides! I'm on a path of discovery, and the teacher is relying on their own experience to help keep me on that path. Unlike an instructor with a fixed curriculum and a list of desired outcomes, my guide does not know where I will wind up, but makes sure I get there as effectively and as safely as possible.

In school, I knew what the instructors were looking for, and I excelled at giving it to them. This does not work on the yoga mat, and I sometimes struggle to be a good yoga student. I need to find my own path, with some markers along the way, instead of trudging down a highway that millions of others have already traveled. I may end up at the same destination, but what's important is to get there on my own problem-solving steam.

The most frustrating, yet empowering, thing my yoga teacher would say when I struggled with a posture was, "you'll figure it out." It must have been challenging for him to do only that. When someone is struggling with something, my urge is to grab the wheel, so to speak, and do it for them.

When I'm leading a large yoga class, I'm spread quite thinly. But even here, there are moments when I can drop some words of wisdom or do a quick demo—actively teach—if I see that it will benefit the majority of the class. Although this is a somewhat hit-and-miss approach—give them some instructions based on rules of thumb and hope they're suitable for this group—it's still useful, even if some students don't see a practical application of the concept until later.

The important distinction I see between instructing and teaching is the instructor acts like a how-to manual, while the teacher accesses multiple options in their experience to find a path that best suits the person they're working with. Teaching is less efficient in a big group, simply because everyone has different needs. Imagine the accomplishment if kids had access to individualized teaching at all times!

Off the yoga mat, I remember times when an instructor became a teacher for me, and they changed my mindset significantly. In my last year of design school, my thesis project, a bathing system for elderly people, crashed and burned during a mid-year review with professors and peers. In retrospect my work wasn't ready for the review, nor was I mentally ready for the negative feedback. The criticism so deeply affected me that I was lost for weeks afterwards, my confidence destroyed. As a result, my other minor projects were a mess as well. I didn't know what I was doing, and I was ashamed that this was happening to me in my final year when I was supposed to be at the top of my game. Thankfully, I at least had the wherewithal to approach a professor whose opinion I trusted and tell him just that: "I don't know what I'm doing". I was literally on the verge of tears as this came out. I didn't know what I was looking for from him, but he did. He closed the door, sat down, and said, "Well, you're either in love, or you're having a creative crisis. Assuming it's a creative issue (wink), I have found that when I'm between creative plateaus like this, I just need to hold on, be patient, keep working, and it will sort itself out. You'll see." We didn't talk for more than five minutes, but this was enough reassurance to me that I felt like I had a lifeline. Over the course of the remaining weeks in the term, things worked out fine.

My professor became a teacher in that he let go of academia, thought broadly about the issue, related his own personal experience, and then, without telling me anything specific to my project, reassured me that I had the capacity to fix it. He guided me to success. He did not tell me what to do.

In day-to-day life, a teacher gives me that extra push, or that extra piece of information at just the right time when I'm at a plateau or struggling to reach it. They may even point out that I've plateaued when I didn't know it myself. Maybe they're an actual teacher, or maybe they're a civilian who's popped into my life at just the right time to get me back on course. They might not even be aware of the role they're playing.

Everyone is a teacher, whether they know it or not—modeling behavior, inspiring people, leading them...for better or worse. An objective third party, hopefully someone with more experience who can provide feedback on what they see and tips for what they feel might help me improve, is a rare and valuable gift that deserves acknowledgement.

I guide people best when I've experienced what I'm trying to teach. There may sometimes be something I haven't experienced, but I can still help. I identify the problem or challenge, develop some solutions and then try them out. If a student is game and I'm honest, this can work. I cannot drop my torso backwards to land my hands on the ground into a wheel. But I can do a fairly deep backbend, and I know what's needed for the physical and mental preparation.

I know the details of how to do this posture because, paradoxically, it's really hard for me to do it. Some people who can do this posture easily have the advantage of a body that is primed for it, but their limited body awareness means they don't actually know how they've solved the puzzle. It has taken me a long time to understand the importance of identifying the problem before coming up with a solution. A backbend may look like it takes flexibility to avoid injury, but sometimes strength is more useful. Very often when a solution is implemented and doesn't work, it's because the effort has not been put into determining what the real, fundamental problem is. This is true in medicine, finance, engineering, and yes, yoga. How can I teach someone if I don't know what they need to learn?

All of this is to say that teaching takes vigilance. It's best treated as an organic form of communication, an exchange of ideas, tests, and results. I have to balance a deep understanding of myself and of my students to help them find their way. Teaching yoga is a humbling way to see my personal impact on those around me, to savor it, to be surprised, and to maybe make some changes to how I see my role. I have to be on my toes—an active presence—the whole time. If I'm exhausted at the end of a session, even if I've barely moved, I know I've taught well and learned something too.

My 'self' is housed in this organic machine that enables me to interact with the world. My job is to take care of my body so that I can continue to interact with the world for as long as possible. My body continually sends me signals to keep me updated on just how well things are going. And, these signals are opportunities for me to learn about the world, and in doing so, improve my 'self'. And sometimes, like all humans, I ignore the signals and get sick or injured, which albeit unpleasant, is still a way for me to learn. I instruct my body, and my body teaches me.

**I am not my body. My body is my teacher.**

Sometimes I'll take a moment, look at my hands, and be glad for the body I have and what I learn from it. I vow to protect it and to keep it functioning well. It's my vehicle for interacting with this beautiful world, and it's the only one I've got.

## STUNTED

I am stunted.

A friend in a brand-new relationship was looking for advice. I was at a loss. Twenty-five years with my husband means that I'm underdeveloped in how to date.

Another friend is a hardcore Cross Fitter. He goes to the gym every day and eats a ton of chicken breasts. He's got massive calves and quads. He came to a yoga session with his seventy-two-year-old mother and couldn't kneel down on the floor, unlike her.

The reality of circumstances—geography, upbringing, peers, education, food—means nobody is perfectly well-rounded. The key is to address where my life is functioning well and where it needs some nourishing. This applies to my mind, my body, my relationships, and my work.

Will I give up my marriage to gain dating skills? No—that's a horrible tradeoff for me. So why am I feeling somewhat lacking next to my dating friend? Maybe this tells me something about my other relationships. Is there an opportunity to put myself out there and make more platonic friends?

Should my CrossFit friend be able to do what his mother can on the yoga mat? Not everything—everyone's body is different. He can bench press twice her weight. She can almost do the splits. Practicing next to each other is an opportunity to find where they each need work, but also to understand that effort within the context of their own goals and limitations.

The quiet focus of yoga gives me the mental and physical space to see where I can improve, but even more importantly to ask if those areas actually need improving in the first place. Lacking ability in something does not necessarily mean I must rectify it. I've never been able to throw a ball well. Despite the odd cultural pressure on men to be able to throw, as if this skill would at some point be lifesaving, I'm okay never gaining that particular skill. I can't be good at everything, nor do I need to fix something that is not broken. However, my lack of throwing ability does beg the question: is there weakness in my arms or shoulders that could be improved and perhaps as a result add some longevity to the joints? This is a worthwhile inquiry and will likely bring positive, functionally useful results.

**Everyone is working from a different set of imbalances.**

We've lived different lives, slept differently, eaten different foods, moved in different ways, and experienced different joy and sadness. Yoga evens things out, bringing imbalances into focus so that I can objectively determine where I need to catch up, and maybe where an imbalance doesn't really matter.

## CULTURE

"Yoga" is Japanese for yoga. Who'd have thought?

I was in Tokyo a few years ago and attended yoga classes at a few different studios. I wanted to know what yoga was like in a foreign place. A Japanese friend had given me a list of studios with classes offered in English. As it turns out, an English class is still conducted in Japanese. A teacher asked, "so you don't speak any Japanese at all?" I guess it's unusual for a visitor to spend part of a trip trudging around doing yoga classes, so they probably assumed I lived there, and like all expats, had no choice but to learn the language. I shook my head sheepishly. They seemed worried.

The studios were lovely. Everyone was welcoming. In one class, all of the students introduced themselves to me. The familiarity of the studio setting was incongruous with my utter lack of knowledge of Japanese words. I have so little understanding of the language that I didn't even know when someone was asking me a question or making a statement. But I felt so included that it didn't occur to me that my smiling nod might not have been responding to a greeting, but to "That's my spot you're sitting in, dummy."

On another level, the experience got me thinking about "style of yoga" versus "teaching style." One of the classes was Jivamukti, which I had never tried before. Apart from having China Gel rubbed on my back and shoulders by the instructor while I was in a posture (I'm such a sucker for any form of attention that she could have rubbed me with manure and I would have felt special), everything was familiar. A fellow student asked me after class what style of yoga I practice. I really wanted to say Hatha because that's the correct answer, but I found myself stumbling to mutter a few varieties that I've tried over the years. I think it's important for teachers and practitioners to remember the distinction between style of yoga and teaching style. Jivamukti, Anusara, and Vinyasa are not styles of yoga—they're styles of teaching, and they're all just different ways of getting to the same thing. Not being able to understand what was being said in the Japanese classes made this even more clear, since the opening dialogue and spoken adjustments generally are the only things that separate one style from another.

The only downside to yoga in a foreign place: within about a minute of starting one of the classes, I had to pee. The prospect of rudely disappearing or of trying to announce to the whole class that I was not adult enough to go before the session and that I needed to know where the toilet was, encouraged me to stay put. And I was fine. From this I learned yoga takes your mind off peeing, whether you're in Tokyo, Berlin, or presumably even Niagara Falls.

What I learned: yoga is not owned by anyone; we all share it, and barriers are erased when a class starts. It's an activity that bears a universal language (the actual language, Sanskrit, of course, but also the tone and intent of the class) supported by many years of history and understanding. This got me thinking: what else connects me to others? Yoga is not the only thing. It occurred to me that barriers between cultures are a construct, and the concept of culture shock is maybe something made up to explain jetlag and grouchiness.

**What I eat, how I dress, where I live: these are all variations on the same, basic human needs—food, clothing, and shelter—regardless of culture.**

There's never a culture that announces, "Oh, we don't eat. How odd that you put those substances in your mouth. How vulgar." In the yoga studio, we have all agreed to share an experience, whose history is outside the birth culture of most of us. We have discovered that yoga resonates with us. Yoga shows me I have the ability to adapt to and to make the most of—enjoy, even—whatever is dished out. I appreciate the shared language of yoga; it's a reminder of all the hard work we've done on our own paths, and yet those paths intersect as if we're not just sharing present experiences, but also past ones.

## PRACTICE

The importance of "practice" is the biggest takeaway for me from my yoga experience. As a child, practice was encouraged. As an adult, I feel like the world expects me to know how to do something or not to do it at all. Yoga reminds me that practice is central to all success, including to the achievement of my own well-being.

I find it helpful to think of practice in these components:

**motivation—learning—repetition—patience**

I practice so that I can get better at something, whether it's balancing a peanut on my nose or performing cardiopulmonary resuscitation (CPR). This is not possible without some degree of reflection on the experience, the parsing of the information, and the evolution or advancement of my understanding of it. In other words: learning. If I'm not actively learning, I'm simply going through the motions and repeating the same activity over and over, like a habit.

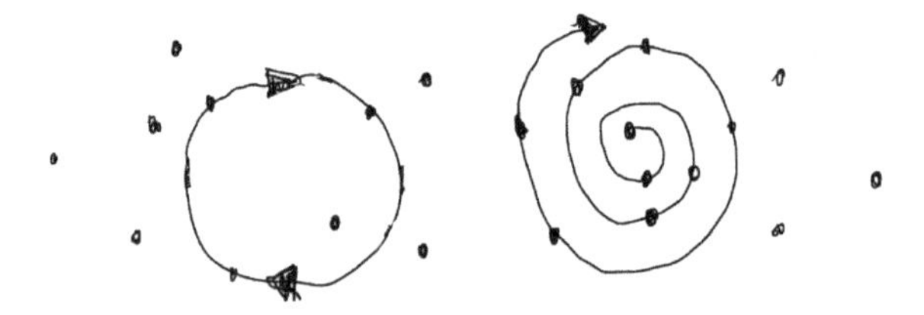

I see habit as a circular path that just keeps encountering the same things I already know. Practice is a spiral, where I'm continually encountering and learning new things.

**The difference between a practice and a habit is learning.**

Brushing my teeth, taking a shower, doing dishes: most of the time the tasks are performed in "habit" mode. These are automatic—they've been done many times and can be repeated easily. There's no explicit need to improve, so there's also no learning and no reflection.

For some habits that are considered "bad"—smoking, social media, nail-biting, gossip, cynicism, eating chips—if deep reflection is involved, some interesting thing can happen to help end the habit. I've noticed that when I'm acting on a bad habit, I'm on a self-indulgent autopilot. So I try to flip the switch and turn these bad habits into a practice, where I'm fully conscious of my actions at all times. I try to get really good at them. Biting my nails turns into trimming my nails with clippers. I gain the capacity to put an end to that habit because I'm more fully in control and realize that the physical effects and the emotions surrounding biting my nails do not feel good. Caring for my nails and establishing a new routine feels good, and I'm able to consciously choose this new alternative. It's an interesting thought exercise to consider how to hone smoking, gossip, or social media skills to turn these habits into active, controllable choices, where they can actually evolve into constructive activities.

**By becoming more aware of my bad habits, I can gain the objectivity to abandon them.**

Similarly, if I consider something to be a good habit (hygiene, text etiquette), I take the same approach: look at the habit, explore the physical and mental effects of the habit, and try to get better at it. Practice it. Why? Maybe improving this habit is not necessary, but using a familiar task as a focus for improvement is a nice way to avoid complacency. It keeps my mind from wandering to some dark places, and it's good training for tackling the bad habits. This ongoing practice of reflection and self-improvement gives me a sense of progress during times when other things in my life might be stalled. And, pretty much every time I've reflected on a good habit that I thought I'd been performing well, I've realized there was room for improvement. My teeth are whiter now.

When I'm on the mat, I need to remind myself I'm practicing. My ego makes this so easy to forget: disappointment creeps in when I miss a posture, or if my stamina is low. What's wrong with me today? If I remind myself that I'm practicing, the anxiety dissipates, and interestingly my performance improves. I'm focusing on the task at hand as opposed to my expectations or aspirations, and I'm more tuned in to the mechanics of my brain and body. I'm savoring the practice.

**I practice yoga to improve how I interact with my body and my surroundings.**

When I remind frustrated students of this, some of them nod but I know they don't buy it. They think accepting their moderate improvement (or failure) is a cop-out excuse. They don't understand that a big part of the challenge is acceptance itself, and through that they will progress. Their frustration is actually creating an even bigger barrier.

I see students deal with practice on the mat in two ways: by following through or jumping ship. People sometimes get so fixated on perfecting a small portion of the postures that they lose sight of the bigger picture. They jump ship, and immediately restart, not allowing themselves to proceed until they've nailed that one thing which, unfortunately, just gets them even more frustrated. They don't experience the affirmative sense of completion that will motivate them to get back to it another day with rest and a fresh outlook. So I always encourage people to "follow through" with every sequence. If they're tired, lose their balance, or feel sloppy, I tell them to keep going until they've completed it. It might be messy and almost farcical, but that's part of the vulnerability necessary to learning. Then, all they need to do next time is "clean it up."

There is a guarantee that real, mindful practice will lead to progress. I try things. I experiment. I evaluate. I hold onto the positive trial—the one that gets me closer to my goal—and let go of the negative one. If I'm muddled, and it seems like I might be falling into a habit and not learning much, sometimes a break from practicing is helpful. Distance can give me an objective assurance that I'm on the right track. Magically, spending some time away from whatever I'm fixated on makes me better at it.

A yoga practice does not have to be a big production: a few postures in the morning or at night, and I've progressed. Sometimes I take it further. I only need a two by six-foot piece of floor. I don't need a mat. I can be naked. I can be in a tux. While traveling, I do a yoga practice most mornings amid the clutter in very small hotel rooms. It lasts about four minutes. That's all I need to slip into my body, and to remind myself that I am my own portable wellness machine that is constantly changing, learning, and therefore improving.

The beauty of yoga poses is that they're pretty much infinitely challenging. Once I've managed to twist myself into one, a teacher will show me how to take it to the next level. I won't be ready, but I'll always have something to practice.

Practicing postures on a yoga mat brings me through all of the victories and failures I experience in daily life. The difference is that I'm fully in control of my time and my progress. If something is not working one day, I let it go and work on it again the next day. Over time, I connect this phenomenon to things off the mat that are less in my control, but where I can conjure the same relaxed patience in the face of obstacles, discouragement, successes, and delays. My mind goes through the same process. Because my body is not as involved in problem-solving in front of my computer as it is when I'm on my mat is irrelevant. The mind and the self are the common denominator, and my body is simply a tool I sometimes employ.

**When I see "living" as a practice, I realize that no challenge that I encounter is "all or nothing". What I perceive as failure always contains at least a grain of progress.**

## TRAINING

Two questions I often get from beginning yogis are: "How often do you practice yoga," and "Do you do anything else?" My yoga practice is crucial, and I aim to practice five times a week, and yet yoga is not enough.

Movement is good for me: biking, walking, running, dancing. Yoga is designed specifically to round out what's missing from my physical activities, it brings symmetry to my body, and it enhances and informs my other physical pursuits. Yoga has made me a better mover.

As such, my yoga practice can be supplemented with off-the-mat applications. Two or three times a week I'll jog just over two miles. Yoga has helped me bring mindfulness, rhythm, and steady breathing to the twenty minutes I'm on the road. I enjoy it now, and I didn't before. It's a way for me to connect my body and brain to the outside world. To maintain good cardio-vascular health, I need to do this.

Three times a week I lift weights. I'm glad that I have the foundation of yoga to approach the weight training with the right form and breathing. In return, the weights have accelerated my ability to achieve certain advanced postures.

As I write this, I realize that I do very little dedicated mental training. In the past I went to therapy every week, during some good times and some bad ones. I miss it and plan to resume therapy soon. I encounter mental challenges every day—interacting with friends and students, and managing negative thoughts—but I have not set aside time specifically to work on my mind, especially not in a professional setting where I can make time to think about my thoughts. Interestingly, I'm comfortable asking friends or students if they go to the gym, but I hesitate to ask if they go to therapy, because there is still a cultural stigma. I look forward to a time when this is not the case, and everyone speaks proudly of their mental therapy accomplishments.

The reality of my modern-day existence is that most of my mental and physical training is in a "lab". I don't run two miles in a hurry to get somewhere or to escape; I run to an arbitrary destination, then run back. I don't hoist hay bales onto a truck; I lift precisely constructed weights for the sake of lifting. So it feels quite special when what I've learned in the gym, on the running path, or in a therapist's office gets put into practice: a gratifying, real-life sense of accomplishment. Staying calm in a confrontational exchange with a neighbor, or easily lifting boxes into a friend's moving van justifies the hours of practice.

I've had baseball players, bodybuilders, dancers, golfers, martial artists, tennis players, runners, and swimmers—some professional and some amateur—come to me for yoga. They've heard about the benefits, and given their dedication to their bodies, they know that their own activity is also not enough. They're ready for the practice, but that does not make it any easier. In the same way that I, after months of intense yoga training, was surprised that I needed to tap into a different kind of stamina to play tennis, they were a wet mess on the mat by the end of the session.

Yoga shows where work is needed and if that work might need

to happen off the mat. Despite some very intense yoga practices that made my heart race, the movements on the mat do not subject my cardio-vascular system to the same, prolonged strengthening of a thirty-minute jog, or even a brisk walk. But yoga has given me the skill to run and breathe effectively. My shoulders tend to be weak, and targeted weight training has helped me to avoid injuries that often happen to yogis who overdo certain advanced postures. Here too, paradoxically, yoga has helped protect my form as I do strength training for my shoulders.

I have students whose lives are in such chaos that, despite the calm and confidence that yoga can build, I suggest they seek a therapist. Similarly, students with chronic shoulder or knee pain might need to take a break from certain yoga postures and seek targeted physical therapy. Yoga exposes the gaps in my physical or mental health and helps me to understand that sometimes a different activity, whose practice can be immensely informed by yoga, is simply the best thing to do.

## A PLATEAU

I've come to understand that when I'm most frustrated with my practice, when I feel like I'm just not advancing and I'm at a loss for how to proceed, I've likely left one comfortable plateau and I'm working hard to make it to the next one.

Here's an example: I can balance both knees on my elbows, tilt forward and lift my feet until only my hands are on the ground. This posture is called crow, or bakasana. But balancing with only one knee and the other leg extended up in the air is a whole other thing.

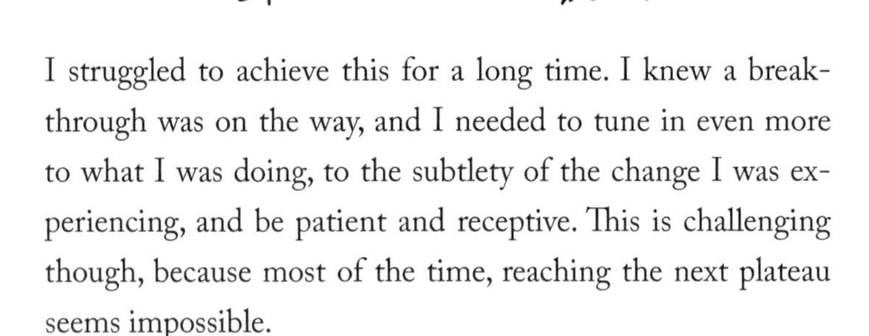

I struggled to achieve this for a long time. I knew a breakthrough was on the way, and I needed to tune in even more to what I was doing, to the subtlety of the change I was experiencing, and be patient and receptive. This is challenging though, because most of the time, reaching the next plateau seems impossible.

This is very similar to the creative process, and the frustration and self-doubt that happens with every project. In fact, what worries me is the times I don't experience even a little bit of anxiety and doubt. Am I not pushing myself enough? Am I missing something? Where's the bottleneck? Of course,

I don't search out struggle—I'm not a yoga martyr—but I do need to make sure I don't become complacent.

The measured, controlled nature of a yoga practice helps me to remember, manage, and accept the importance of these transition periods. There's a lot to orchestrate, and in a good practice I'm fully aware at all times of my performance through breathing and posture adjustments. This is subtle and very internal, and it's exhausting in the most fulfilling way.

**The time between plateaus is when I'm the most vulnerable, but also the most vigilant.**

The reality I've accepted through yoga is that life is a never-ending ascent, with a series of plateaus where I can rest for a while, collect myself, and then move on. And the inescapability of this climb is not dreadful; seeing the climbing parts of my life as periods of transformation is insightful, and arguably more valuable, and certainly more interesting than the comfort of the plateau. I've learned it's okay to set up a tent on the plateaus, but not to build a house. The whole mountain is beautiful, and each period that I'm struggling to move upward I'm gaining strength and confidence. It gets easier, but it's never effortless.

## MEMORY

Since I've been practicing yoga, I've noticed that I'm really good at *Rummikub.*

*Rummikub* is a game of colored numbers on a series of tiles, where the goal is to swap tiles around the table to form sequences. The key is being able to remember multiple sequences of operations until it's your turn, and then execute them. I'm shocked at my ability to remember a sequence of moves in the game. I think I'm good at this game because of yoga.

One of my yoga teachers would lead many of his classes with up to half an hour spent working through multiple postures on one side of the body without any repetition, and then finally repeat the sequence on the other side of the body. It was an amazing experience that left me lost and flustered at times. This was not only training my body, but also my memory. By following him so deeply into these complex sequences, my mind had no choice but to work. In fact, at times I could tell the teacher himself almost lost the thread, but he could rely on some very experienced practitioners in the class for cues. Over time, there was a calmness that took hold, and I learned to treat each posture as a mnemonic for the next; one move reminds me of the next move. This was helpful in the sense that it removed the intimidation of feeling the need to remember the whole sequence, knowing that I just needed to remember one step at a time, and to trust that the next one would reveal itself soon enough.

I now apply this same trust in my memory when I teach students myself, and most of the time make it through a seventy-five-minute class without any errors. I have seen many of my students strengthen their own "memory confidence" in much the same way. Consciously or not, they're feeling out the transitions and using the sensations in their bodies as their own mnemonic devices, whether it's to make any number of tiny adjustments within a posture or transitioning between postures in a continuous sequence. It's choreography, basically.

Dancers of course have this ability too—their livelihood depends on it. Dance is one of my favorite things to watch live. I'm always astonished by dancers' ability to learn and execute a minutes-long choreography, paired to music, and often synchronized with other dancers.

If I falter—let my mind wander—while I'm teaching or practicing, the whole sequence can be temporarily thrown. So in addition to helping me maintain a strong memory, yoga is helping me to cultivate a focus, an ability to stay engaged in the task at hand for its duration.

My body keeps my mind from wandering. I remind my students of their ever-strengthening mind-body connection, and the tools they're creating for themselves on the mat to manage the realities of time, age, and change. A deepened awareness of my body, my sheer sense of presence in my body, also deepens my mental awareness.

**A strong and flexible body has helped give me a strong and flexible mind.**

# HEALTH

Eat well. Sleep well. Exercise well. Good advice, right? Unfortunately, the opposite is still lauded: who can get by on the least amount of sleep, how great it is to indulge in junk food, and how horrible it feels to exercise. Hopefully this attitude will change soon.

I want to go about my daily life with ease. When I'm unwell physically or mentally, I'm experiencing "dis-ease." If I can identify the source of the dis-ease, internal or external to me, then I'm more likely to be able to create a plan to correct it. But how do I identify the source?

1. **Go to the doctor.**

2. **Learn about my body.**

3. **Do some physical or mental therapy.**

Early on, I had an expectation that others—experts—would fix my problems for me. But my experience with physical and mental therapy helped me put the responsibility back on myself, and to take an active role in my own well-being, both proactively and reactively. This was an important awakening.

I'm saddened and a little frustrated when someone tells me, "I went to therapy for a while, but it didn't work. So I stopped." I'm glad they took the initiative to first go to therapy, and then to stop when they did not experience a benefit, but it does beg the question of why didn't it "work"? What was their expectation of "work"? Maybe their therapist was not a good match. With the right professional, therapy can work. But it takes patience, hard work, an open mind, and constant self-reflection.

One night a few years back, before I started teaching yoga, I was finding it difficult to read in bed. In my peripheral vision, the text was sharp, but when I looked straight at a word, the letters swam. In the morning light, I noticed a perfect circle of discoloration in the middle of my field of vision. Despite the severity of this symptom, I only booked a doctor appointment after a friend took me by the shoulder and said, "This could be brain stuff. Go."

At first, the ophthalmologist shrugged and told me this was the reality of aging. Sigh. I was in my thirties. But then he paused and took another look. His expression went from dismissive to concerned, and he made an appointment for me to see a specialist that day. He said nothing, and I was scared.

I spent the afternoon undergoing tests. The diagnosis: a retinopathy. Cells in my eye were dying and creating holes that let fluid leak out and accumulate behind my retina. This was distorting my vision. How was it that cells were dying? "Stress", the doctor said. *Stress*. What can I do about it? "Don't be stressed." The irony of the stressfulness of the diagnosis was not lost on me. But she also pointed out that just identifying the cause is a reassurance that often puts people on the path to recovery. This is true for spine, shoulder, foot, and wrist injuries too: if they're less mysterious, I am more equipped from a practical standpoint to start to heal. And, perhaps more importantly, I'm just a bit more relaxed about it, just a bit less scared and intimidated, and this helps me heal much more effectively.

She also suggested I take a yoga class. Of course, at the time I was dismissive of that option. How could moving through poses with a classful of people reduce stress and fix my eyes? I now understand that the question for me was: my brain was affecting my body—could I leverage my body to affect my brain? Yoga has since helped me realize the answer is: yes. This experience was direct evidence that stress contributes to disease. The solution—stress reduction—was not only a remedy to the issue at hand but serves double-duty as a prevention of future stress, the ill effect of which can manifest itself in a wide range of physical and mental ailments. Yes, yoga relaxes me, thereby reducing stress, but it goes beyond that. Its proactive promotion of self-inquiry, self-awareness, and self-regulation is fundamental to my well-being.

What I've just described is not meant to trivialize or suggest that what is known more conventionally as devastating "disease", like multiple sclerosis or cancer, is easily remedied. But the steps are still the same: go to a doctor, learn about my body, engage in therapy—physical, medicinal, surgical, mental—and do everything in my power to slow, halt, or hopefully remove the symptoms.

When I used to get sick, I'd forget how it felt to be healthy; I felt like I'd always be sick. For years, when I caught a cold, I paid no attention to the process of "getting better". I was either sick or I wasn't, then one day I'd wake up and feel okay. The incremental changes that I have learned to observe in yoga have helped me understand the complex mechanism of my body healing itself. This is an important distinction:

**Medicine and therapy do not heal me, they correct the circumstances within which my body and mind can heal themselves.**

My only responsibility is to seek out the help I need for this to happen. When I'm sick now, my deepened self-awareness helps me trust my ability to get better, and the hopelessness that I felt in the past does not appear. Being pro-active and informed does wonders to find some form of recovery, and also helps to set realistic and sustainable expectations, however severe the symptoms.

## RESILIENCE

I think of resilience as a measure of how quickly I bounce back from a trauma. By definition, all trauma isn't necessarily severe. A car accident or the death of a loved one have strong emotions attached to them and lengthy recovery times. They're without question traumatic. But a sprained ankle or a bad customer service experience are also traumas, and without even minor resilience, they can be disabling. Unfortunately, I can only build my resilience by testing it. Yoga is a safe, practical, and controlled way to do this.

Yoga postures are hard and take time and patience. People struggle with this and want to give up. Some students have told me exactly that—thankfully after their session. "To be honest, I was overwhelmed and tired, and wanted to leave." But they didn't, and they succeeded in building their resilience a tiny bit more; resultingly, their next practice session was that much easier.

### Resilience is hard to measure.

I can run a mile every day, yet still be tired by the end. It feels like nothing is improving. But it's likely I'm running faster each time and my stamina is increasing.

I had a student a while back who was in the midst of trying to save his faltering business. He was hoping that yoga would be an escape for him, and a chance to unwind. The few sessions he did were very gentle, yet even moving a little exhausted him and made him feel nauseated. Yoga was starting to make him feel worse, but he felt like he needed to get his money's worth by working up a sweat. It's possible he was out of shape, but I had him start with very easy postures. He claimed his recent doctor visit gave him a clean bill of health. So what was going on?

Perhaps he lacked resilience; his mental immune system, so to speak, was shot, and this state was manifesting itself in a physical reaction. Like for his business, there was no quick solution to get him physically and mentally back on track. It would take time and work, which he did not want to hear. It's possible he was running his business this way too: hitting his head against a brick wall rather than stepping back to evaluate the circumstances, listening to trusted advisors, and changing course. He was hardened by circumstances.

**Resilience is strength, but it's also flexibility.**

Like this student, many people think of yoga as an escape. But the movement and sensations on the mat are a reflection of my ongoing mental and physical state, and I need to find comfort and stability there. If I'm ignoring what I'm feeling, then I'm not practicing yoga. There might be a temporary reprieve from directly addressing the stressors in my life, but ultimately yoga builds an alternate way to help me face these challenges head-on, not to avoid them.

After a couple of years of horrible fights and infidelity, my parents divorced. I was seventeen. For about a year after that, I encountered my first bout of depression. It was oddly novel to me; my surroundings appeared dim and cold. I literally thought things around me had changed, not that my perception was skewed. I now understand that I had reached a tipping point, and my mind was reeling from my circumstances. I had a solid set of friends and talked a great deal about what I was feeling. I was lucky. I thought a lot about what happened to me, and this first experience with mental illness was also my first experience with building resilience through deepened self-awareness.

Similarly, during a very challenging yoga practice at the beginning of my training, I heard, and felt, a pop in my right knee. We had been doing a series of crossed-leg postures that I was following somewhat blindly to keep up with everyone. My hip joint was evidently not flexible enough to take on the torque in my knee, and I tore a tendon—a sprain. I felt sick to my stomach. I finished the practice and hobbled out of the studio, a little embarrassed that I did not have the control to avoid such an injury. There was an odd machismo in the locker room as well, and the only support I received from fellow students was "Yeah, that stuff happens sometimes." The pain over the course of the next couple of weeks made it impossible to tax that joint any more, luckily, or else I likely would have continued to damage it. Eventually the injury healed, and the trauma taught me something about my body. In doing so, I gained some resilience, but a different kind. Physically, I learned that I needed to gain flexibility and strength in other parts of my body to protect my knee. Mentally, the resilience helped me not to panic with future traumas. I also obtained a kind of pre-emptive resilience from the experience: I had been cavalier and ignorant, and now I was vigilant.

Of course, I'm not explicitly looking to be injured to broaden my life experiences, nor am I seeking out a crisis so that

I can work through it on the mat. Those things will happen by themselves! I'm reassured by the knowledge that when a trauma does happen, I can face it, manage it, and heal to be more resilient the next time around. Yoga presents me with an opportunity to build resilience when I'm not recovering from something—when I'm feeling good, not feeling horrible. This is a useful shift in my approach that I now apply to other facets of my life.

**Unfortunately, a life without trauma is impossible.**

If someone came close to shielding themselves from all trauma until late in life, if and when a traumatic experience did occur, however minor, it would be catastrophic. A fender bender might cause them to never drive again. A stubbed toe might ruin a month of activities. The death of a loved one might put them into such a spiral of despair and pain, and ultimately poor health that they put themselves at risk of dying.

If yoga builds resilience in my body, might it not also be building it in my mind? A yoga practice is a period of time when I can focus on just myself. Invariably, traumas surface on the mat that might otherwise stay hidden: an injured ankle, a sore shoulder, and yes—guilt, anger, and resentment stemming from past experiences. My body and mind are working together in harmony to process trauma and build resilience. I create obstacles—traumas—for myself. I give myself the time and space to experiment, learn, and progress. I challenge myself to deepen certain postures, and to try others. I accomplish postures I didn't think I could, and as a result I'm equipped to face things I didn't think I could off the mat. My body becomes stronger and more flexible with each movement, and so does my mind.

## POSTURE

My posture—the way I stand and sit—has a significant impact on my life, and my life is reflected in my posture. The tilt and unevenness of my shoulders, the curvature of my neck, the roundness of my upper back reversing itself into the arch of my lower back—all of this was formed by years of physical and mental experiences: leaning into a desk, mouse under one hand, keyboard under the other; lying in bed with my arms and legs askew; unconsciously spreading my shoulders and raising my chest with confidence during the best of times; or letting my shoulders round forward and slumping with fear or discouragement during the worst of times.

**My posture is a physical manifestation of my personality and my mood.**

I tend to walk and sit very upright, which for a long time I saw as healthy and ideal. I now understand this as unnecessarily tense and rigid, leading to neck fatigue and pain. Who am I trying to trick into thinking I'm in control and approachable, that I'm not a monster? With a bit of focus, I find a balance of engagement and relaxation, and look somewhat normal.

I see this in my students as well, and the older they are, the more pronounced. Two of my elderly students, unknown to each other, crane their necks forward and round their upper backs. To them, this is a normal, relaxed posture. If I adjust them manually and ask them to hold that position, despite how awkward the sensation is to them, I literally see years drop away in an instant. In discussions, I learned that despite their career successes, they have always felt that they had to work hard to be heard and understood. They literally push their faces forward in conversation to make sure they are connecting with their listener, who is usually sitting back, passive, relaxed, and happy to have them do all the work.

This possible physical manifestation of their personalities was revelatory to them and unfortunately caused them some resentment. Why had they burdened themselves for so long to be understood? They were crippling themselves in service of others. An adjustment to their posture can help an adjustment to their interpersonal dynamic. It will take work and practice, but the physical changes will be a gauge of their progress.

With these two students, there was a straightforward strategy to correct posture on the yoga mat: strengthening the back of the neck, bringing their shoulder blades together, arching the lower back. With others, the posture adjustments are more complex. The imbalances surface during a practice when I see which asana, or pose, is more challenging for them. Sometimes one side of the body struggles more than the other, revealing an asymmetry that was not visible when they were standing or sitting. When this happens, it's an opportunity to discuss why, and it's fascinating for me and for the student to dig a little to identify what in their life is manifesting itself in their body this way. Sometimes it's how they sleep or drive, and sometimes it's an irritating co-worker beside them who they've been subconsciously turning away from for days, months, or years on end.

Yoga identifies and fixes imbalances through the repetition of poses or "postures". The simplicity of the approach is astonishing when compared to the depth of transformation: I move my body through a series of full-body strength and flexibility-based "shapes", and the result is relief from months or years of suffering. Proprioception—awareness and control of my body's position in space from my fingers to my toes—also improves, which preempts future imbalances.

I remind myself that in yoga, I'm not practicing for the sake of the shapes I create with my body; the poses are a vehicle for practicing control—a deep orchestration of breath, movement, and focus that ultimately has a positive impact on my physical and mental postures.

## BREATHING

Breathing is central to a yoga practice. Rationally, it's central to all activities, because they wouldn't be possible without it. But the difference with yoga is that there's a focused opportunity to get better at breathing.

The two things that high-quality breathing impacts are stamina and stability. If I'm breathing well, I can sustain what I'm doing more steadily and for longer. What makes for a high-quality breath? Slow and deep.

Ancient yogis believed that humans have a fixed lifetime's worth of energy inside them, and rapid, shallow breathing allows that energy to dissipate more quickly, thus shortening a lifespan. Slow and deep breathing conserves that energy and extends life. Science has shown us this is mostly right; if I breathe deeply and slowly, my heart rate slows. Slow, deep breathing during physical exertion is enabled by a strong heart, which means I'm taking care of myself with lots of physical activity. Breathing also taps into my central nervous system; if I breathe slowly, I'm calmer. One long breath gets the same amount of oxygen into my bloodstream as several short, shallow breaths. But this is hard to do. Yoga helps, since breathing is paired with movement; I have an anchor that guides the depth and duration of each breath. But this is also one of the most challenging aspects of a yoga practice.

One of my students was recovering from a gunshot wound to his upper leg. His injury, unsurprisingly, made it difficult for him to balance. His leg was numb from nerve damage, and his muscles were not cooperating. This was functionally inconvenient for him and mentally distracting given the residual emotional trauma from the event itself. He used to be in the military and had an admirable level of resilience, however, and a willingness to work hard, which is what brought him to me. Session after session, though, I found that his injury was literally a thorn in his side. Forward lunges, single leg balancing, and even some symmetrical and mostly stable postures left him wobbly and staggering.

I realized one day that I had been so focused on his leg that I had not been aware of his breathing. So we stopped and worked on seated breathing for a bit and then resumed the standing practice. Once he was breathing with intention and more evenly—pairing the breath with the movements, for example, exhaling as he lifted a leg forward, and inhaling as he lowered it—his balance improved immediately. What happened? In addition to slow, steady breathing calming him down and reducing his frustration, the controlled inhalation and exhalation had a mechanical effect: it stabilized the muscles in his abdomen and pelvis. What started as wobbly, unpredictable, and labored postures turned into smooth, easeful transitions.

In yoga asana practice, when I'm pairing movement with breath, all breathing—inhale and exhale—happens through the nose. My nose is designed for breathing. The mouth is a backup. Nose breathing controls the volume of air and slows me down. Yoga does not require any sudden movements; here are plenty of other ways in daily life to practice that! There are a handful of techniques involving mouth breathing, but always while in a static position: sitting, standing, or lying down—not while moving. Otherwise, my nose is the port of entry and exit.

I simplify breathing for students into three facets: breathe slowly, inhale into expansive movements like reaching upward, and exhale into contractive movements like folding foward. There is a lot to orchestrate on the yoga mat, and this generally helps keep people on track.

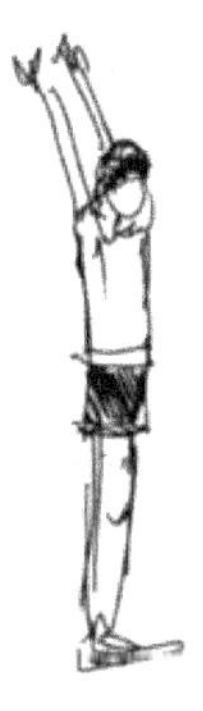

When I'm practicing, I time myself in postures by counting breaths. This way, I'm forced to witness my breathing, keep it slow, and any urgency I bring to the mat dissolves; it feels like I have all the time in the world. Physiologically, my breathing connects my brain to my body via my central nervous system, and the result is relaxation and focus. There is a subtle but important difference between letting my breath drive the movement, which relaxes me despite the exertion, and letting the movement drive the breath, which tires me out.

In some ways, yoga is breathing. I sit up straight. I inhale. I exhale. I do it again and slow it down. There, I've just done some yoga. I try it again and let out a big sigh as I exhale. There, more yoga. Then, I start to combine movement with the breath. As soon as my breathing is sacrificed in favor of movement, I'm no longer doing yoga and must pause. I like this approach, but it takes a discipline that can be quite intimidating.

Sometimes I find it helpful to make a humming sound as I exhale through my nose, with my mouth closed. I've just made a sound similar to an *Om*, which is often used during a yoga session to breathe more slowly and a little more calmly. If I'm in a group, at first, it's a bit conspicuous to make any noise. But it's freeing, like singing in the shower.

I went through a brief phase where every time I made the *Om* sound, especially with a group, I'd want to cry. I was no longer just feeling the breath in my nose and chest, I was feeling it in my whole body. Adding a sound to breathing— amplifying the vibration—deepens the impact of the breath. It makes breathing more real, and I feel more committed to it. This blend of confidence and vulnerability took some getting used to, but because I can not only lengthen my breath but also modulate it is a very impactful realization. This is second nature to a singer; for me it was yoga that helped me understand how breathing is a full-body activity. My breathing is a way to harmoniously connect my inner self—something that's literally happening inside me, both physically and emotionally—to my external self and to my surroundings. Like all other aspects of yoga, good breathing takes practice and has a big payoff.

Now, my yoga breathing helps me with running and other activities, physically exerting or not. It's probably the most useful tool I have to calm myself down, conserve energy, dissolve any irrational or negative thoughts, and to feel in control, especially when everything around me feels like it's spinning.

## CHANTING

To chant is to sing. In French, to sing is simply *chanter*. But there's some stigma attached to chanting; it's often associated with Gregorian monks or some type of cult-induced ritual. But it's actually just another healthy way to exercise my body and brain.

Chanting with others reminds me that we share a similar, beautiful, organic mechanism. If I'm chanting, I'm breathing in a controlled, sustained, audible way. I'm proving I'm breathing and savoring it. And, because I lack musical tone, it's a nice way to sneak in some singing without any expectation of hitting a particular note. Chants have lyrics, and in yoga they're in Sanskrit. Some of the chants are a series of syllables designed to create a certain acoustic resonance, and others are spiritual, and acknowledge the student-teacher bond, or a higher power. In a group, the effect can be quite impactful and uplifting.

**There are three components to chanting: breathing, vibration, and memory.**

I can't chant without breathing, so I'm forced to practice and gain control of my breath. The vibration starts in my throat, but I can start to feel it in my whole body, like getting a massage from the inside out. It feels good and oddly cleansing, like a deep, loud yawn. I need to use my brain to remember the words. Usually, it's an easy phrase that gets repeated over and over again, so it's a confidence boost that I don't need a photographic memory. When I was five years old, I sang "I'd Like to Teach the World to Sing" at my kindergarten graduation.

I haven't really done any solo public singing since. For me, chanting started as quite an awkward activity but eventually gave me a sense of confidence in an unexplored facet of my self.

Periodically I chant a simple *Om* during my own practice, but I rarely use chanting during my teaching sessions. Recently, however, three students were in the studio, and we were working on elongated breaths. Despite the intimacy of the space, I just couldn't hear them—I couldn't tell if they were managing to control their breath or not. I realized they were hiding in the silence. This is a group of two men and one woman, all in their seventies, and they tend to avoid the spiritual aspects of yoga. They don't like savasana—they keep their eyes open and tap their fingers impatiently. They don't like even thirty seconds of sitting quietly (I don't dare call it meditation) at the beginning or the end of a session.

I realized the only way I was going to be able to help with their breathing was to have them chant. But I didn't tell them this; I had them sigh as loudly and for as long as possible. Then, I had them make an "ahh" sound for as long as possible, like they were at the doctor getting a throat exam. I was very detailed with my real-life analogies, and they were very close to making the *Om* sound, but I didn't push it. At the end of the seventy-five minutes, I had them breathe with intention again, this time on their own without my guidance. I asked how it went, and one of them replied, "Yeah, it was fine this time since you weren't talking anymore." I didn't mind the snark, given I had managed to get them to chant.

These students found it difficult to elongate their breaths, but had no trouble making a long, slow noise, which is basically a slow exhale. (Other people can talk for long periods without inhaling. We all know someone like that!) Making a sound, whether it's a chant, an Om, or simply a sigh is a good way to bring attention to breathing, and eventually this can transition to long, silent breaths.

A friend has recently begun to experience aches and what he describes as constriction in his neck and throat. His voice, as a result, is also constricted. He holds his chin retracted and shoulders forward, and his breath is shallow. He's a warm and loving friend, but he also holds himself back, not wanting to impose himself on his surroundings. I don't know why. I've suggested he try chanting—singing—as a way to relax his throat and neck. I know that his voice will become lower and gentler, the aches will subside, and his outward persona will be a more authentic reflection of what's inside him.

A chant, starting with a simple, elongated ohm is a nice way to acquaint myself with the subtlety of breathing. It's yoga for my throat—airway, vocal cords, neck muscles—which needs to balance strength and flexibility just like other parts of my body. Talking is not enough; it's staccato and too focused on content. A controlled, elongated vibration from chanting is designed to smooth out the kinks so that, when the time comes every day, I can communicate in a relaxed, easeful way.

**A strong and flexible throat brings a depth and richness—grace—to my voice that has a positive impact on the dynamic I create with others.**

## PHYSIOLOGY

Many students ask me to describe the perfect form for a particular pose. There isn't one. There's a history to yoga poses, and a "suggested" form for each one designed for an optimal combination of stretching and strengthening. But the reality is that everyone's body is shaped differently, is incredibly asymmetrical, and is weaker, stronger, stiffer and more flexible in different ways. To achieve the most benefit, the posture therefore needs to be a little different for everyone.

If I'm in a lunge and my back tends to arch by default, then maybe I should work on straightening it a little to strengthen my abdominal muscles or stretch my hip flexors and quads or both.

I've had baseball players in my studio for a series of sessions to help with their shoulders and backs. Years of training to throw and swing had, despite their overall good health and athleticism, thrown their bodies into astonishing asymmetry and pain. One of them was in his early twenties and had already had elbow surgery. I described a yoga practice to them as a way to undo what our bodies undergo throughout the day. For some, it's hours of sitting in front of a computer or driving. For them, it was hours of twisting and flicking.

I don't believe that everyone needs to have a deep understanding of anatomy and the mechanics of movement. I tell people it's okay to have variations on postures as long as it's based on a deepened awareness of their own body position—their posture—and where there might be an imbalance or a risk of injury or both. Yoga teaches me to move with intention, and in doing so, to understand my limitations and where I can stand to do some work.

I try to keep things simple in my own practice and in what I teach others:

1. My pelvis is central to the mechanical function of my body, and so it gets the most attention in my practice. My upper body (front and back) connects downward to my pelvic bone, and my lower body (front and back) connects upward to my pelvic bone. Stretching and strengthening the front and back of my upper and lower body need to happen in every yoga practice so that my posture stays shaped as designed—factory settings, so to speak.

2. If one side is stronger or more flexible, I spend twice the amount of time working the other side until it seems like it has caught up.

3. Strength + Flexibility = Balance. Physically, balance is not a mysterious skill that comes and goes; a combination of strength and flexibility in my muscles keeps me from falling over whether I'm on two feet, one foot, or one hand.

4. Advanced postures do not benefit me more physically than mid-level ones. I practice advanced postures to chal-

lenge my brain, which sometimes means overcoming fear.

5. My shoulders and knees are delicate and must be treated with care. The muscles, tendons, and cartilage in these joints cannot bear a lot of force, so I need to make sure the adjacent muscles are strong enough to do all they can to protect them.

6. Adjacent joints are often the culprit in injuries—if my elbow is sore, it might be my shoulder that's to blame. If my knee is sore, I might need to look at my hip joint for clues.

7. Breathing is integral to my practice. Every movement gets a breath, either an inhale when my body is expanding, or an exhale when it's compressing. Breathing with intention stabilizes my muscles and helps my stamina.

8. Sweating is crucial when I'm physically active. My body's cooling mechanism covers me in water that interacts with my surroundings to evaporate, thereby cooling the surface of my skin. I don't pat myself dry; not only is this a distraction, it prevents me from regulating my temperature.

9. A simple *Sun Salutation* gets me most of what I need as a foundation. I can add variations to that for fun and to keep it interesting. Backbend, lunge, pushup, pushback, squat...a sun salutation is the base structure for many more complex yoga sequences, but it in itself is plenty for a thorough wakeup of body and mind.

Effective movement takes effort. There is no short cut, despite how fitness fads are portrayed in advertising. It takes time to throw my body out of alignment, and so it takes time to regain that alignment in a way that can be sustained. The good news is that there is a lot of smart, reliable help available: teachers, videos, and classes. I need to have a "sense" of my body and understand how it works in very simple terms. Through learning and experimentation, I can create and maintain a positive physical state.

## STRENGTH, FLEXIBILITY, AND BALANCE

My left arm is stronger than my right one. My right foot turns inward a little when I stand, and that makes me wobble when I'm balancing on that leg. I'm confident speaking to large crowds of people but falter in small groups. Driving to a location does not mean that I'll be able to find it again unassisted. I could go on.

There are things about me that are well-developed and other things that just aren't. Circumstances—family, upbringing, preferences, opportunities, relationships, jobs, athletics, and food—make me behave differently and present different levels of pain, pleasure, joy, and comfort.

Strength, balance, and flexibility are the pillars of yoga, and they support not just the physical side of the practice, but also the mental. I like how neatly everything fits into one of these categories. Even the most advanced yoga postures can be dissected to just a combination of strength, flexibility, and balance.

Physically, it's easy to see where there are gaps; either I can or can't do a pushup, stand on one foot, or touch my toes. This is a direct result of certain muscles being too weak or too stiff.

Physical strength—the force my muscles can exert, and their stamina—is also straightforward to address: lifting weights and practicing yoga. Weights can be used to isolate muscles and target their conditioning, and yoga takes care of muscle groups, conditioning them to work together in complex ways.

Physical flexibility is often considered the opposite of strength, but it's not. I want my muscles to be strong and flexible. The work is not mutually exclusive. As I'm building strength, the more I can lengthen my muscles by stretching and make sure the acquired length is cumulative by stretching often, the more mobile I'll be when reaching, twisting, and bending.

Physical balance—the ability to not fall over—relies on an intricate combination of strength and flexibility. It's also a fairly straightforward concept to evaluate and address, barring any brain, nerve, or inner ear malfunctions. Humans have extraordinary balance, proven by the sheer act of standing up: I'm occupying a tiny amount of floor space with my feet, yet I'm orchestrating my muscles firing, as a second nature, to keep from falling over. I can even keep my balance when I'm on my toes, and thereby reduce my footprint even more. Yet, when I reverse this and try to do a handstand, it's much harder. A handstand takes arm strength, which I have, but I revert to an infant's pre-walking sense of balance when I'm upside-down: teetering and momentary. My body can do it, but my brain is not ready.

But mentally—how strong, flexible, and balanced I am in my outlook—is where the gauge is more abstract. To make things even more complicated: often the physical limitations or achievements I'm experiencing are a reflection of my mental state. That's where I really need to stop and think, especially when I'm practicing a more challenging posture like a handstand. Recently, a posture I had been working on was finally only possible when I realized it wasn't physical flexibility I needed, but physical strength. My mind had stubbornly fixated on one path to a solution, and it was wrong. The significance of this concept in terms of life decisions was not lost on me: sometimes, I might think it's softness I need, but really, it's resilience. I think about the times where I've thought it best to defer to others' opinions, when really it might have benefitted everyone for me to be firmer, more vocal, or more direct.

Similarly, "muscling through" something physical or mental never works in the long term; finding the right combination of strength and flexibility takes reflection and practice. I've had a handful of students in my studio who have started their yoga practice with this mentality—force their way into a posture—and it has only resulted in frustration and sometimes injury. Suggesting they try to find comfort and relaxation in a posture that they're approaching with full-body engagement seems absurd to them, but understanding this distinction is really where their work lies.

My father died unexpectedly in 2004. He was in a bicycle accident. I had encountered emotional traumas before, but they had all been things that I could overcome and try to fix. I could be strong to get through them. But the permanence of his death was something I could not undo. People offered words of strength at the time, but I had trouble processing this; my mind spun, and spun, and spun. I understand now that the only way I could deal with his passing was with flexibility. I did have to be strong enough to take care of myself and to make sure the trauma of his death didn't somehow bring about a trauma of my own. My family's future had changed: he would no longer be in it. The situation was a done deal, and to stay happy and healthy we had to let the circumstances gently unfold to reveal how we fit into this new reality.

**I can't control all circumstances, but I can roll with them.**

Before I started to teach a large number of older students, I assumed most people over seventy were physically and mentally inflexible, from years of hardening experiences. I now see the opposite in so many of the seniors who visit my studio: their age and wisdom have given them a unique balance. Maybe some of them rediscover their younger flexibility on the yoga mat—a willingness to try new things and deal with the challenges that are put in front of them—but it seems to be with a different mindset than what I see in younger students. Their experience has made them kinder to themselves. They know their limits and hold their ground, but they're game to learn. It's a subtle difference, and quite inspiring.

I've assembled a list of synonyms for each of the three pillars to help me think more broadly about their significance and their impact on my life:

**strength: resilience, firmness, power**

**flexibility: softness, patience**

**balance: moderation, harmony, grace**

To progress in yoga, I need to face what I'm missing and work on recalibrating myself. Do I need to be stronger, more resilient? Do I need to be more flexible, softer? Do I need to balance, and maybe moderate? Similarly, when something is not working in my life, I ask myself the same question: am I lacking strength, flexibility, or balance? It's a helpful question that usually leads to a solution, or at least to a path. When

I increase strength, flexibility, and balance in my body and mind, I feel more stable, and can move forward with confidence and grace.

## PAIN

Sometimes, yoga hurts.

I'm always careful not to use the word "pain" during sessions. I downplay what students might be feeling by calling it 'discomfort'. Smart, huh? But for the sake of clarity here, let's call it pain.

Pain is my brain's interpretation of a signal my body is sending to convince me to back off—removing my hand from a hot stove, or not walking with a shattered femur. This is helpful, and I learn from it starting the day I'm born. But the residual effects of pain, after the actual pain has gone away, can be quite confusing.

Pain carries a lot of baggage. I was taught as a child that if anything at all caused pain, I should stay away from it. And if I injured myself, I should never again do whatever it was that lead to that injury. As a result, I think I missed out on a lot of fun stuff. My fear of pain became a sort of pre-emptive pain in itself, like a child crying out in pain before the doctor has even inserted the needle. In yogic philosophy, an attempt to avoid all suffering simply brings about more suffering.

Pain and fear are intertwined. That's mostly useful. The problem is that I'm bad at understanding the difference. My brain tells me something is painful, that it might cause me harm and that I should be afraid of it, when this is not always the case.

I've worked hard to understand the nature of pain and the limits it creates. When I stretch, it hurts. When I use muscles I'm not used to using, it hurts. When I go for a longer run and have trouble breathing, it hurts. When I feel that I've been misunderstood, it hurts. When a loved one passes away, it hurts. These are all very different kinds of pain. How much of any trauma can I safely endure? This is a very difficult question to answer because the limit changes all the time. When I see friends and family encounter pain, I can empathize with them and offer some form of comfort; however differently pain might be handled by everyone, it also connects us all.

I find it more useful to think about the positive result of pain: resilience. In many ways it's the opposite of pain. And paradoxically, the way to build resilience is to experience and accept pain. On the yoga mat, the way to safely expand my limits is not to ignore the pain, but to use it as a guide through a slow and steady exploration of a posture. I have found this to be true off the mat as well. Bad things have happened that caused me pain, but I'm glad for them. They have made me vigilant, strengthened me and prepared me for the inevitability of more bad things.

Pain's value extends beyond trauma prevention: yes, it can be a distraction that prevents me from getting things done, but it also keeps me present. My mind does not wander if I'm experiencing discomfort in a posture. Pain keeps me aware and focused, and I learn to manage pain on the yoga mat in a controlled, safe way. Then, I'm more equipped to manage the pain I encounter off the mat under sometimes chaotic circumstances.

**Pain is a thorny hedge that lines the path to comfort; it tells me where my ever-changing limits are, and guides me to a new, stable, and safe level of achievement.**

## INJURY

My mind and body are connected. They are in constant communication and need each other to survive and grow. They can heal each other, but they can also damage each other.

Despite my first knee injury during yoga many years ago, it happened again recently. Once again, I heard a loud pop!, felt a sudden jolt of pain, followed by a tightening of the joint, nausea, and fear. This second time, which happened on the other knee and was during my own self-guided practice, took me by surprise—I know yoga! I teach people how to avoid injuries! How could this happen? Well, I learned that, even at this advanced stage of practice, I don't know a lot. I wasn't tackled in a football game. I didn't fall off a ladder. I was performing a set of slow and steady transitions with a bent and twisted leg, and the force went to the path of least resistance: my knee. I had pushed too far past my limits, and for a moment lost sight of my body, hell-bent on getting into the final posture. Looking back, there were warning signs that I ignored, and didn't connect to knee issues until it was too late. My hip was stiff, and I had felt pain in my kneecap while squatting. Something was not stable in the joint and I ignored it.

"Mind over matter" is a way to overcome injuries temporarily, particularly if there are greater forces to get past to avoid further pain. This is not an effective long-term plan—I do need to get out of a burning car even if my leg is broken, but I must not ignore my broken leg forever. I need to face, evaluate, and heal injuries as soon as is practically possible; open wounds need to be sterilized and dressed.

**Not acknowledging an injury does not make it go away; it seals it into a container, away from view, and lets it rot.**

The same is true with more abstract, and definitely more stigmatized mental injuries. Sometimes, I experience for a day or two what I can only describe as mental pain. It slows me down, like a paralysis of some kind. My mind spins, and I can't let go of certain thoughts, just like a physical injury with chronic pain serves as a constant reminder of that trauma. If I can manage to reflect on what's going on during these times, it always points to an injury. It's not necessarily a catastrophic event; a disagreement with a trusted friend is an injury. When I have a stack-up of similar mental injuries, I reach a tipping point where I reflexively retreat and feel depressed or anxious. I don't want to do any activities, and so my physical well-being suffers too. And, I feel guilty about this because the injury is invisible. Nobody is going to question a broken leg, but I'm worried people will question the time required to recover from a disappointment, especially if it's only one small part of a larger, historical pattern. But this is nonetheless an injury, and once I recognize it as such, the path to recovery is clearer.

My yoga practice is an exploration of my limits. They change every day, and they're a result of my life experiences, both physical and psychological. If I ignore those limits because I'm distracted or motivated by something other than the exploration and learning, I risk injury. This is true whether I'm cooking, driving, putting on my socks, or interacting with loved ones. A lack of presence can have bad, or even disastrous, consequences. I'm glad to have had injuries on the yoga mat; the context acts like a safe practice run where I can experience, accept, and move on from the negative experience, be it a sprained knee or a bruised ego. If and when something happens off the mat, I'm equipped. I'm less shaken and have a more acute awareness of cause and effect, which will ultimately render the recovery process more efficient.

## RECOVERY

Yoga does not fix me. Yoga provides the context in which my body and mind fix themselves.

I didn't understand my body's capacity to heal itself until I started practicing yoga. I knew that if I had a cut, my skin would heal—but that was the extent of it. The idea that my muscles, bones, ligaments, and brain can do the same thing, invisibly and unremarkably, is astonishing. It's also very reassuring.

To find the road to recovery, I find it helpful to think of my mental and physical ailments in two ways: traumatic or cumulative. In doing so, I'm also identifying the steps I might need to take to reverse the injury, or at least to avoid it in the future.

**Injuries can be sudden or cumulative. Sometimes it's hard to tell the difference.**

For example, sometimes I have less serious injuries: a twisted knee, a sprained ankle, a slipped disc, a pulled shoulder muscle. These injuries are either traumatic, meaning they happened suddenly from a fall or a sneeze, or they're cumulative, meaning they happened over time, like hunching over a computer every day or doing a lot of driving. Sometimes it's a combination of the two. During my first yoga training module, I developed 'tennis elbow' in both arms that was so severe that I had trouble lifting a book. What started as a minor, almost imperceptible injury from repeated aggravation reached a tipping point when, without a chance to heal, it was suddenly so painful that it seemed to have come out of nowhere. Identifying the cause of the injury was the first step to recovery. I attended sessions with a physical therapist and discovered I was overusing certain shoulder muscles in a movement similar to a push-up, and this was affecting my elbows. I took a break from the posture at issue, which had become nearly impossible to do anyway. I did some gentle strength training, gave it time, and the pain went away. Ultimately, I learned to make an adjustment to my shoulder and hand position in the push-up posture—chaturanga—to avoid a recurrence of the injury.

Sleep is a good context for recovery, provided that I am not unknowingly aggravating an injury. With my injured shoulders and painful elbows, it took me a while to realize that despite all the care I was taking to heal, every night I was spending eight hours making it worse, tossing and turning, lying on my sides, legs and arms askew. When it finally dawned on me that my sleeping position could be at play, the realization itself got me partway to fixing the pattern. I worked to find comfort on my back, lying as symmetrically as my flawed body would allow, so that at least at the start of the night I was set up for success. Over time, I managed to sleep differently, and my shoulder healed more effectively. Here, like in so many other situations, the accumulation of tiny changes, the small bits of practice, the slightly deepened awareness, paid off.

A couple of years ago, I rejoiced at managing to run a mile. That's because one afternoon a month earlier, I went from effortless handstands to barely walking. I had agreed to open-heart surgery to repair a congenital valve defect diagnosed eight years earlier. My doctor figured since I was healthy and still only mildly affected by the blood regurgitation, as they call it, it was a good time to get it fixed. After six hours on the operating table attended to by a team of skilled doctors, nurses, and a robot, I woke up in the ICU covered in tape and tubes, my brain fuzzy with anesthetic, my arms and legs restrained to keep me from reflexively pulling out my attachments. My husband smiled nervously as they removed the breathing tube from my throat, and I strained to understand my circumstances. I thought they had yet to start the surgery, but it had already been eight hours.

There are many claims in the wellness industry that are so vague, so oversimplified with shallow logic, that it's no wonder they are dismissed by western medicine as magical thinking. Detoxing! Fasting! Coconut oil! Turmeric! Kale! Colonics! Sound baths! Infrared saunas! All promise a quick fix to what ails me. Mainstream ideas of wellness are kooky. This is a shame because real wellness, I finally understand, was central to my surgery, care, and recovery. I literally cried with wonder at my body's capacity to self-correct during my time in the hospital. (Admittedly, the medications might have played a part in my emotions.) Now I have first-hand evidence of what's important for wellness, and it's not just kale: moderation, movement, socializing, trust, self-awareness, nourishment, rest, and consistency. The time, trials, patience, and learning of a holistic yoga practice equipped me with mental and physical resilience that I did not have at diagnosis eight years earlier. Before and after the surgery, I had to put aside my untested notions of wellness and trust my body and the experts around me. The nurses and doctors in the ICU were my yoga masters: their years of experience got me standing three hours after my surgery and walking twelve hours later. They guided every movement, body function, and reaction. Twice I walked too eagerly and began to shiver uncontrollably. This passed. I had time-lapse hallucinations and polka-dot blind spots. I urinated gallons. I was soaked with sweat at night. I coughed for two days straight. I thought these were setbacks. No, these were signs of my body regaining control as the anesthetic and trauma subsided. The ICU team nodded with approval at each report during their rounds.

I was home in five days. Two weeks later I was back to teaching yoga. (I say this not with pride but with astonishment.) My own asana practice hurt too much to return to, except for *savasana*, the restorative properties of which were a first-hand revelation to me. I walked and jogged. I did laundry. I cooked. I made the bed. The residual pain forced a new kind of mindfulness that in turn caused me to relearn many practical movements. I feared sneezing and coughing because it felt like my ribs would tear apart at the incision, but I marveled at the other limitations that broadened my self-awareness. I had been taught that there is nobility in pushing myself. No. There is nobility in holistic self-awareness, and if pushing myself is necessary, then I push myself. My new take on the value of yoga: tiny, incremental improvements in strength, flexibility, and balance bring a joyful, sustainable wellness.

**A sustained mile of running just a month after heart surgery was more of a reflection of a decade of yoga than a handstand was.**

I periodically tell injured students the best thing for them is not to do yoga. My body is designed to heal, inside and out. My job is to retreat, protect my wounds, and then take the necessary time to mobilize. Active people often mistake this approach for "doing nothing", and resist. This is not the idea. I do need to stay active, but in ways that work around the injured area without aggravating it.

**Yoga itself does not heal me. Yoga gives me the tools and resilience to manage my body and mind so that I can heal myself.**

And I love aggravating my injuries! A remote student of mine has a five-day per week yoga practice at her local studio, in addition to various cross-training activities. She's in excellent shape, and her yoga practice is precise and quite advanced. And yet...she had a nagging, painful tear in one of her hamstrings, her shoulder was in constant pain, and periodically she'd have headaches that extended from the base of her skull up over to her forehead. She's very body-aware and had noticed that the headaches were triggered by her yoga practice. Rationally, she knew she needed to give herself time to heal, but she continued to push herself in the hopes that ongoing work with her muscles would relieve the pain. It's even possible that the mental stress from her injuries was worsening them while she practiced. Her biggest challenge was to do nothing.

She now understands that her body is not doing nothing when she's doing nothing. That's when it's doing the most to try to fix itself. By pushing through her injuries, she was actively preventing this beautiful phenomenon from taking place.

I asked her to consider this: if she has a cut on her arm, will it heal faster by rubbing it with sandpaper? Keeping it clean and leaving it alone is clearly the right thing. This applies to all injuries. Remarkably, scars left from healing wind up being stronger than the surrounding tissue. Cells learn their lesson.

**My mind is also designed to heal itself.**

When I've at times been dulled by depression, the mental state has manifested itself physically as sluggishness, slow reactions and speech, and fatigue. I've managed to nudge myself from it by a bit of familiar movement, but sometimes this kind of physical retreat from a mental trauma is necessary—a chance to recalibrate. But here too I have to be careful that the retreat is not filled with the things that injured my psyche in the first place—in these times it might be conflict, loss, failure, or discouragement. I need to protect myself from further triggers and then work on the things surrounding the injury to make sure it doesn't happen again. Or if it's bound to happen again, hopefully the resilience gained will lessen the blow and speed up the next recovery session.

So here's a simple approach to recovery from physical and mental injuries:

**retreat—protect—mobilize**

Retreat from the cause of the injury and stay away so that it does not get worse. However, sometimes it's a challenge to identify an injury's true cause.

Protect, clean, and cover my wounds. If it's a mental injury, that means working to not let it creep into all aspects of my life. "Hygiene" is a concept that applies beyond washing my hands; it's about being physically clean, of course, but also relates to a mental cleanliness, and also to a cleanliness in my surroundings. Throw out the trash, don't hoard it.

Mobilize and stay active. Work on the surrounding tissue or thoughts so they can compensate for my temporary immobility, and build up some resilience. If I have a sprained ankle, I can still find a way to use the rest of my leg. Then when body and mind have had some time to heal, target that area gently and precisely to get it back in the game. Thoughtful, incremental improvements are the key.

A handful of times, I've had new students in my studio for private sessions who were in the midst of such intense physical or mental crises or both, that it was just about impossible to have them do anything other than sit and breathe. This may seem trivial to an outsider, but for someone who is suffering deeply, the commitment to getting better and to doing even one tiny thing like getting out of the house—not to mention committing to something new—is a big step to recovery.

I should note that, often, other forms of therapy are advisable. I've encountered students who use yoga as a way to avoid mental therapy, and this might be wrong—they're resorting to something maybe more familiar when perhaps they need to expose themselves to unfamiliar territory to progress.

As I've deepened my understanding of the mind-body connection, I've realized that a limitation appearing in an unexpected place can be the result of an imbalance or trauma in a seemingly unrelated area. My injured shoulders caused my elbow pain. The loss of my father—the grief I experienced—made it hard for me to do public speaking. My work stress caused failures in my vision. Trauma is sneaky. The vigilance gained from yoga can help to identify each trauma's true nature.

I respect my changing limits and seek help when I need it. Yoga can play a big part in healing, both in terms of the physical and mental benefits of the practice itself, but also in how the process and patience it demands sets a tone for other facets of my recovery plan. Do I feel better after yoga than before? If the answer is yes, which it is most of the time, then I know yoga is helping with my recovery.

**At the end of a yoga session I'm by no means healed, but I usually feel just a bit better than when I started, which is a realistic, achievable goal.**

## REST

It's a good thing I enjoy sleeping, because I literally cannot live without it. It's a chance for my body to recover from the day's physical activities, repairing tissue in organs and muscles, and it's a chance for my brain to sort and store memories from the day, as well as to wash away the toxins that have accumulated. The recommended eight hours of sleep per day is necessary downtime for full-body maintenance.

I perform better when I'm well-rested, and yet I feel guilty that I've taken that time. I'm surrounded by messages that big accomplishments on very little sleep, despite the scientifically proven benefits of bedtime and naptime, are aspirational feats. But this is not true; any genius in a sleep-deprived haze performs well in spite of the lack of rest, not because of it, and the performance is not sustainable. During major project deadlines in design school, one of my professors reminded everyone in the studio that there were not eight hours in a day, but twenty-four. Most of us nodded ambitiously, and these words served as permission to pull multiple all-nighters to get our work done, including operating dangerous model-making machinery. I now understand we were idiots. It was a vicious cycle—the less sleep I got, the more poorly I performed and the slower I worked, which resulted in more sleepless nights to get projects done. After many years of practicing and teaching yoga, I'm only now starting to see the extent of the restorative properties of lying on my back, on the ground, arms at my sides, for a few minutes a day.

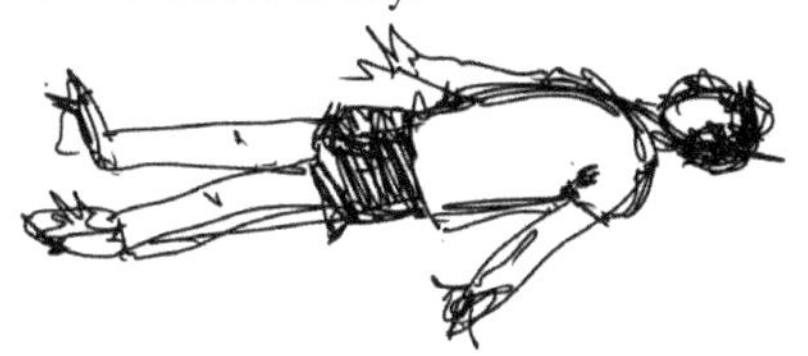

The floor and gravity are good tools to reset my body. *Savasana*, or corpse pose, is yoga's form of rest, and it's very valuable and very difficult—and it's different from sleeping. I see clients fidgeting, talking, opening their eyes, or, understandably, falling asleep. They're waiting, not experiencing. One of my students, who I know does not like sitting idly, recently made it through seven minutes of *savasana*. This was not a long time, yet when I asked her how long she thought it was, she replied "too long."

I understood. When I first starting practicing *savasana*, I myself didn't close my eyes; it somehow made me feel vulnerable, less in control. In reality it was the opposite: I was not able to control my mind enough to trust that my surroundings would not do something unexpected. I now realize I also didn't want to face my own thoughts.

I end all yoga sessions with *savasana*, mostly because the fatigue from the session helps to put my clients in a relaxed state. They often welcome the break and treat it as a reward. But it's a posture like all the others and takes time and awareness to reap the benefits. Physically, the posture allows my bones and muscles to settle into a passive, regenerative state from the much more active. I'm horizontal, so my heart works less to get blood pumping against gravity. I can feel the effect of my lungs massaging my ribcage and stomach up towards the ceiling and down into the ground with every inhale and exhale. I can feel the weight of my head at the small area at the back that's pressing into the ground, and my facial muscles melting away from either side of my nose. I have to work a little to relax my fingers and feet; they keep wanting to right themselves instead of just drifting out to the sides. My lower back is a little achy and uncomfortable to start with, and there too, once I've consciously relaxed those muscles, I can feel my pelvis roll back into a gentle stretch, front and back. Mentally, I'm relaxing, and in a way, stretching as well. I'm letting my mind uncoil, not directing thoughts one way or another, just letting them pass and sort themselves out. My mind or body might be causing me to fidget. Any initial discomfort I'm feeling is a pretty direct reflection of how much I'm resisting letting go.

The beauty of lying on a barely cushioned floor is that it's soft enough to relax, but not so soft that I fall asleep. Otherwise, I'm missing the opportunity to self-reflect, to observe the wonder of what my body can do entirely on its own.

**_Savasana_ is a way to learn how to sleep—the ultimate restorative state—without actually falling asleep.**

Eventually, the self-regulating part of *savasana* kicks in: what at first, post-workout, felt like the most comfortable thing imaginable, gets... uncomfortable. The back of my head gets a little sore. My body has cooled down and I'm chilled. My hips, having allowed my feet to rotate outward, are a little stiff, as is my lower back. My mind is refreshed, but the obligations of the rest of the day start to creep in.

I'll bring my knees up to my chest, give them a hug, roll side to side, and then sit up. I open my eyes and cross my legs. This, now, is far more comfortable, and gives me a few seconds, just a tiny moment, of insight into meditation: sitting on the ground, with ease, and just observing myself in my surroundings with a physical and mental freshness, and even a bit of wonder. This is how *savasana* is different from sleep—I have not descended into a full REM state, but I've relaxed enough that alpha waves have filled my brain. I'm resting, but I'm still very conscious while my body's organs are recalibrating themselves.

For me, a good *savasana* is a reminder that my body knows how to take care of itself. To go a little deeper, it's an opportunity to reflect on my own humanity, and mortality. I live in a body that has limits, and that will ultimately expire. In *savasana*, I can face this reality with optimism because I'm tapping into and marveling at what it's still able to do. Usually I've spent up to an hour twisting, pulling, balancing, and sweating, and come *savasana* time, I can take pleasure in relinquishing control and observing what my body and brain are going to do next. It's like getting the results from an experiment.

I have clients who are working only on *savasana*. They might not realize it; we go through a whole series of postures, some energizing, some exhausting, and as always, I have them spend some time lying on their backs. Over time, I see their *savasana* improve. It's their capacity to let go, to find comfort in what they see as a vulnerable state that slowly improves, rounding out their physical and mental wellness.

I recommend to everyone that they practice *savasana* each day. Sometimes, that's the only posture I do—post heart surgery, it's the only posture I could do, and at that it was difficult to settle into the ground without irritating my wounds. It's a focused, effective mini vacation. Everything about it—getting down into it, being in it, getting up out of it—is a fundamental, beneficial practice for bodies and minds. It's a central function of being human.

Other forms of rest—taking a break—are important off the yoga mat, and *savasana* has helped me to understand their effect. We have a trailer in the high desert that we escape to every couple of weeks for one night. There is no cell reception, and therefore no internet. There's also no electricity, and therefore no appliances and lights buzzing subtly. I didn't know these sounds were disruptive until they were gone. Like in *savasana*, when we first get to the trailer, I feel vulnerable. I don't have the comfort of connectivity, and in many ways, I'm forced to relinquish control. In doing so, my body and brain take over to repair or undo the burdens I've heaped upon them over the course of the week. I sleep very well, and return to the city refreshed and clear-headed, as if I've had a veil removed from my face. I feel like we've been gone for a week, and it's been less than twenty-four hours. Rest—practicing *savasana*, sleeping, doing nothing—restores the functions of my body and mind.

**I start to rest as a monster, in pain and foul-minded, and emerge refreshed and friendly.**

I appreciate the wonders and importance of rest. There's something very special in the idea that I can relinquish control completely and things that have been bothering me physically and mentally get fixed without my active involvement. I need to create the time and place for the repair work to happen—book the vacation—and the "rest" takes care of itself.

## POLLUTION

I know that my yoga studio needs to be uncluttered for me to get the most out of my practice. But what about the things that surround me for the rest of my waking hours? Perhaps this is an even more important aspect of my physical and mental health to examine.

Clutter, taken up a notch, is pollution. I know this is true with respect to the environment. What starts as a few bits of litter strewn about very quickly turns into a garbage island, with devastating, toxic effects that take a toll on the planet and on my body: poor air quality, poisonous water, and a broken food supply. This is a relatively straightforward issue to play a part in addressing, although not everyone does their part: recycling, reusing, consuming less, and protecting nature.

But what about my mind? Cluttered surroundings are definitely a distraction from focus, and to a great degree I can exert some control over that. But the news feed on my phone, the attitudes of some people around me, the movies and television shows I encounter every day: I've started to see all of that as a different type of pollution.

I used to watch a lot of shows about zombies. I was telling a friend about one, and he said he just didn't want to watch them because he didn't like the idea that the blood, gore, hate, and violence were entering his brain. This was the first time I had seen certain sensory inputs as pollution, in the same way that I'd see smog or gas fumes, or, for that matter, a deep-fried candy bar.

Now, I ask myself, "Is this good for me?" in the same way that I question whether or not I should eat a certain food. Am I learning something from this television show or movie? Despite the anxiety or horror, is some of the content helpful to my growth? Most of the time the answer is no— life provides enough character-building pollution on a daily basis without the need for self-imposed extras, especially if the only excuse is boredom.

The time on the yoga mat is time away from pollution, where I can start to re-sensitize myself to what does and what doesn't work for me. Off the mat, then, I feel more equipped, more discretionary, to make choices about what to continue to absorb.

# CHANGE

The effect of yoga is cumulative. It's like oiling a cutting block. The wood gets better with age and use, but the scars are still visible; they're ever-evolving and part of the block's history and what gives the block character. In fact, a cutting block without these signs of change does not seem authentic.

I wear my history proudly, and leverage it, but it does not dictate my present or future. The world is constantly changing around me, so how can I not be part of that change? The real question is, how can I manage—direct and accept—change so that I can move forward? How can I transform?

**It takes more effort to resist change than to accept it. Yoga is about learning to embrace change.**

With any new object or activity, I might immediately find it resonates or I might hate it. Simply forcing myself to try it over and over, or competing with others to adopt it, might not alter my reaction. However, there is such a thing as an acquired taste—something that at first I disdained (broccoli, dancing, non-fiction) I later found myself enjoying. This does not happen spontaneously; something about my circumstances has changed, my senses have been refined or dulled, or I've reflected on what triggered my initial disdain to discover that, deep down, there's an aspect of this new object that does resonate with me, and my focus shifts. When my tastes change, I've allowed myself to see the object and its context more broadly.

**To learn is to change.**

Yoga is a process of self-discovery, and even a small commitment to a practice will reveal surprising facets of my self. Discovering I can alter my body and mind—my approach—to do something on the yoga mat that I didn't think possible, is very much like discovering a super-power. This excitement helps me stick to a practice, to continue to learn, and to find my own unique relationship with change.

For most of my brother's younger life, he hated any form of change. My parents put wallpaper up and changed the curtains in our room one fall weekend, and he was distraught over it. A month-long family trip to Germany when he was twelve was torture: different beds, different foods, different people, all exacerbated by jetlag, the ultimate routine destroyer, literally sickened him.

I recently asked him about all of this. He thought about it, and told me that as a child, his reaction to change was a fear of its permanence. Now that he's an adult with kids, and must model behavior for them, his attitude has mellowed. He's able to rationalize his understanding of change: it's not always bad, nor necessarily permanent. He knows that to function, he must accept some degree of change at all times, and in fact some change is positive and progressive. Conversely, some people can take this too far: a "fear of missing out" can prevent people from savoring, even for a short time, the value of the circumstances at hand. But for my brother, the inevitability of change was a bitter pill to swallow that he fortunately managed to rationalize and accept.

The ultimate change—death—happened to our family when our father passed away unexpectedly. My brother sat comfortably, albeit mournfully, with this reality because he realized there was nothing he could do about it. This showed him that his earlier fear of change was rooted in anticipated regret. What if he decided he didn't like the new curtains, or the new school after all? With our father's death, there was not even a tiny chance of a reversal, which is why death can be so terrifying. But when it happened, my brother learned that he was still going to be okay. This may seem like a sudden breakthrough, but it was gradual. Growing up, maturing, and teaching his own kids prepared him for our father's death. Had this happened when we were kids, without a stack-up of tiny "test" changes along the way, he would surely have been far more traumatized.

"Regret anticipation" paralyzes people. Trying a new restaurant, buying a new car, or starting a new relationship are things that not only make some people trepidatious, but actually cause them to self-sabotage, even to the detriment of loved ones' wishes or well-being. I see this in students who are new to my studio; some of the calls I get never result in a visit. Or, after coming once, barriers go up and they never come back. I don't think it's because I'm bad at showing the value of yoga; it's because some people are not quite ready for the ripple effect of the transformation they're facing on the mat. To address change, they need to face their particular circumstances, which can be very intimidating.

The yoga mat is a safe place to experiment with change. I ease new students into comfortable, relaxed movements to build their confidence, and to dispel any fear. Gradually, I encourage them to do more and more challenging postures, always referring back to the ones they know from previous sessions. I take great pleasure in pointing out at the end of a session, "Look at what you've accomplished." Interestingly, despite how significant the transformation might be, its gradual emergence still makes it a wonderful surprise to finally acknowledge. Their confidence sometimes makes them feel as if they've always had the ability, and it's been inside them, waiting to re-appear.

**For some, the only transformation that happens in yoga is allowing their true self—courageous, mindful, thoughtful, flexible, strong, and balanced—to emerge.**

## A CRISIS

Discipline, self-awareness, and resilience keep crises under control. Of course, there can be devastating traumas that occur, but the mind is what sees a crisis. Crisis is contextual; the territory can be unfamiliar, and the situation can be stressful or even terrifying. But there are many examples of individuals unfazed by events that would give others panic attacks. Maybe they've experienced a similar circumstance before and have thereby developed a certain immunity, or maybe they've worked hard to train themselves to be ready for the unexpected. When something bad happens, I interpret it, usually unconsciously, based on two things: how resilient I am and how equipped I am to manage it.

### A crisis forces change.

This is good and bad. The change is usually good, but it's unfortunate that it takes a crisis to make it happen. People sometimes come to my studio in crisis mode. They're there to practice yoga 'when they need it'. They're physically or mentally worn out. They're injured. They're a mess. It's like they're standing in the middle of a burning house and not sure what to do. Without a doubt, yoga helps give them the tools to recover: breathing and relaxation to create a stress-free context to heal mentally or physically or both, and then gradually rebuilding their stamina and resilience. But consider how much less pain everyone would endure if people began to make changes before the house caught fire! With a burning house, like any crisis, there's a chance that by the time the fire trucks arrive, it's beyond salvation. Ask anyone who has witnessed a house on fire, and they'll confirm that it goes down fast.

I've learned, as a result of crises, that if I don't make a decision proactively, someone or something will make it for me, and I might not like the result. Yoga has taught me the value of doing something to strengthen my resilience when I don't feel like I need it—perhaps I feel great. If I do it when I'm at my best, I'm choosing to build my resilience more effectively, and I reap even more long-term benefits. It's preventative medicine: I'll encounter fewer personal crises, and when they do inevitably occur, they will be softened by my outlook and not seem as severe.

**Practicing yoga isn't just like getting a smoke alarm or updated wiring; it's like rebuilding my house with fire-proof materials.**

## TRANSFORMATION

I have discovered that I can lengthen my hamstrings.

Stretching was something that I used to do before or after exercising, when I remembered to. I thought it was helpful, but not that it was cumulative. I did not realize that my body is not 'what you see is what you get', but that I can actively make long-lasting changes to the structures of my muscles, tendons, and bones. An imbalance in the alignment of the vertebra down my spine is something I can fix.

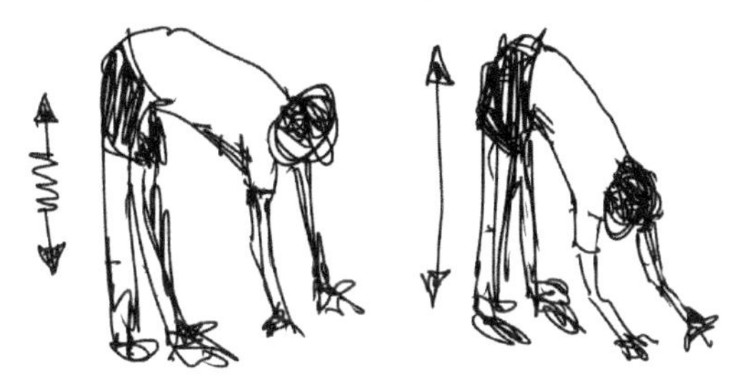

My own capacity to change some of the mechanics of my body also applies to my mind. Yoga has helped me see this. My lengthened hamstrings, allowing me to touch my toes, just like my capacity to find humor in crisis, is a transformation. The way my body works, and my perception of how my mind works, can change and improve. This is a fundamental realization.

With practice, anxiety can be transformed into excitement. Fatigue can be transformed into relaxation. Re-integration of body and brain can reduce blood pressure, lift me from depression, and clear my mind.

I have a tendency to judge the status of something with a

'snapshot' in time, ignorant to progress. Social media, for example, defeats the purpose of yoga because it freezes moments in time. Even before and after shots do not fully communicate the depth of a transformation, and are therefore hollow and possibly counter-productive. A yoga practice is a reflection of my body in flux over time. There's no way to see this other than in person, frequently, day after day.

**An accumulation of daily changes can lead to a major physical or mental transformation.**

Yoga has taught me to be respectful of my limitations, but to approach them with a sense of inquiry, and to know that they can change. I practice. I focus. I savor the small changes and I learn from them; they will lead to larger, life-changing transformations. Time after time, I look back on changes I've wanted to make that seemed far off and daunting, only to later marvel at just how quickly they came about.

## A BREAKTHROUGH

Breakthroughs can seem like sudden, awesome transformations, but they aren't. Breakthroughs are the result of patient, consistent, tiny increments in learning. In other words: practice. A breakthrough can be unexpected, but it's never undue.

And it's the same process at work, home, training a dog not to bark at UPS people, staying off social media for a morning, mastering a new dance move, singing Bohemian Rhapsody uninterrupted, typing without looking at the keys, or mouth-catching a peanut.

This is a one-legged crow. For years, not only could I not do it, but I didn't even understand how to do it. I couldn't get my head around it, even when someone showed me step by step what to do. Then one day, I calmly stepped onto my mat, warmed up a bit, and pulled it off. Now I can do it. I figured out how to ride that bike.

The surprising and somewhat magical thing is that I had not really been practicing this pose. I'd been doing lots of yoga, though, and that was preparation, both mental and physical, for this more advanced posture.

## The work leading to breakthroughs can seem unrelated and even unconscious.

I had been experimenting with adjacent drills and then, there it was! Understandably, the subtlety of context surrounding a breakthrough—I might have had a good nights' sleep, or a good piece of news that boosted my confidence—is also why some things are hard to instruct. I'd had direction twice on how to do this posture, but I just wasn't ready. I needed to trust myself, the process, and the passage of time.

During my early yoga training, as I struggled with a posture, my teacher sometimes told me, "you're not ready. Keep doing this instead," and he'd point to a less advanced, or different posture. This was deflating, but necessary. He trusted that I trusted the process. I had to step up to address not the target posture, but my own limitations.

Off the mat, when I'm struggling to move to the next level in a life, work, physical or mental matter, I try to consider not just the path in front of me, but the adjacent paths that might lead me to success. Time after time, the breakthroughs I've experienced on the yoga mat have proven to have a direct application to my life.

## AGE

As I deepened my yoga practice, I was excited by the new things I was discovering abot myself, and a bit regretful for not having started at a younger age. I think it would have struck a chord then like it does now. However, when I finally immersed myself in yoga, I was a very different person—like a continuing education student at college, with a couple of decades of life experience under my belt. Perhaps because I had a clearer understanding of my own challenges, I assimilated the material very readily. I was my own case study.

**I've always been just the right age to practice yoga.**

It just took me until my forties to realize that. In my mid-twenties, I creaked and ached when I descended to sit on the floor. Incredibly, I did not see this as a lack of fitness, I saw it as a reality of genes and aging. A slightly older friend agreed that his body "really started to deteriorate" when he hit thirty. Luckily, at the time I was surrounded by colleagues who were quite active, and it rubbed off on me. I started riding my bike to work and going to the gym. The creakiness went away. This is also when I first tried yoga, and I uncovered an athleticism in myself that I didn't know was there. Context, circumstance, and camaraderie just made it feel right.

My thirty-year-old friend had established a false demarcation; the human body is constantly changing. It's possible that when he hit thirty it coincided with an illness or injury that caused him to exercise less or to eat differently. From then on, maybe he did not regain his previous fitness level, and blamed it on age. In fact, "I'm just getting old," is the explanation I often hear from people with aches and pains—including many who are not even fifty—who are new to the yoga mat. Honestly, it makes me cringe. But I keep my thoughts to myself because I know that within a few sessions, the stiffness goes away, and they realize that it wasn't aging that was to blame, it was a lack of movement. This is important.

I never considered myself an athlete. In fact, I was disdainful of the idea. I was born into a generation where athleticism was treated as a caste-like system. You either had it or you didn't, just like the assumptions about creativity, math, or singing. It makes me sad to think of it, and I've often said that if I had to teach at a high school, I'd teach Phys Ed. They didn't know what to do with me when I literally ran toward the wrong goal in soccer or couldn't throw a ball more than a few yards. I want to save the teenage version of myself from humiliation and disappointment, and to show him that he can be a drama club nerd and a runner or gymnast.

Looking at my earlier lack of mobility and comparing it with where I am now, I'm heartened and encouraged by the reality that so much is reversible. I can get that flexibility back. I can get that strength back. I can get that balance back. I see it in my students: with a baseline of good health and reasonable mobility, a big part of transformation is confidence. As it gradually restores itself, the physical body can regain what was assumed to be long lost. In fact, I've learned from some of my students that the older they are, the more ready they are for yoga. Maybe crises have prepared them, maybe wisdom.

**Life primes me for my yoga practice; the more living I do, the juicier the material—physical and mental—for me to sort out on the mat.**

In the context of functional training, an eighty-year-old may not be able or willing to work hard enough to do a back flip, but they can regain the mobility they had decades earlier and not think twice about climbing a set of stairs or standing on their toes to twist and reach for something overhead—or, for that matter, simply sitting on the ground and then standing up again.

With younger students, life has not created as many obstacles yet, so a yoga practice maybe isn't as focused. Yoga is of course useful for younger people, but their bodies are still very forgiving, so some of the benefit is not as obvious. But practicing as a youth is an investment, and a great form of prevention.

One reality I've seen is that yoga classes are generally not geared towards elderly people, unless they've been practicing for a long time and can "keep up with" the youngsters. By this I mean keep up with the teacher; large classes are paced at a certain speed and intensity for the sake of scheduling and crowd-pleasing. This is by no means representative of the intention of yoga; it's just the economic reality. Teachers just can't cater to everyone in the room and must operate at a mid-level bar to make sure everyone benefits.

The good news is the teachers who cater to an elderly population are gems. As a teacher, it's easy to bark out instructions to a group of young, agile, strong, injury-free adults. Teaching a session to a group who can't bend their knees is humbling; I was quite embarrassed at my inadequacy when first confronted with this. At the time, unfortunately, my reaction was, "What the hell are they doing in a yoga class? They need to be able to bend their knees." I'm ashamed of that; the immobile students' eagerness and braveness—their gameness—for coming to a yoga class was lost on me. I see it now though, and their energy is contagious and makes me want to work with them all the more. It doesn't matter that they won't do a handstand (maybe they can, or maybe they're just not interested in that). It matters that there's a change from one practice to the next. That's worth celebrating. Teachers who don't get to work with elderly people are missing out on some deep, functional learning.

I've coached a thirteen-year-old and I've coached an eighty-six-year-old. The teenager had mild cerebral palsy, and she was precocious and eager. The senior was quite mobile but was not able to get down on the floor. As I write this, I'm seeing a lot of similarities between the two. They could have been versions of each other: both were calm, engaged, and willing to learn.

I visited my mother just before her 77th birthday. She and her husband had just moved from a house to a condo that's easier to manage and closer to shops and parks. On her birthday the previous year I asked her how old she felt. She thought for a moment, then said, "I guess in my forties or fifties", which was nice to hear and actually true—she has the attitude of someone much younger. I imagine if I were to ask many seniors about their "inside age", they'd say the same thing.

I hadn't seen her in person in a year, and I noticed a decline in her mobility. But I don't think she did, which scared me, but also made sense. I don't notice tiny changes in myself if I'm not actively measuring them. It was a little harder for her to climb stairs, to sit down, and to tie her shoes. Because I'm a horrible, controlling monster of a son, I asked if she was able to sit down on the floor. "Of course!", she said. She resisted demonstrating, though, and I coaxed her (remember: I'm a monster). Then she tried, struggled, and stopped. She was embarrassed and surprised, and scared too. The reality of time and inactivity hit her forty-something inner-self hard.

So we spent a bit of time working on ways to get down on the ground: bending knees, holding a chair, keeping one hand down, the other hand down, one leg out in front, and so on. Then, we worked on getting back up to standing. Her routine from then on was to go from standing to lying on the ground to standing five times a day. That's it. Lie down. Stand up. Lie down. Stand up. It sounds easy but it's not, even for some people half her age.

There was an interesting shift in her spirit when she got into the routine of these movements: she was more confident, more relaxed, and more flexible. Before this, her physical stiffness and instability had begun to manifest itself in her personality. Neither of us had noticed this until she reversed it.

The mind-body connection was so clearly illustrated here that it stays with me as one of the best examples of the positive impacts of yoga on aging. The seemingly simple work of standing up and lying down were proof positive of why she needed to do yoga, and very quickly, that she could do yoga.

Since then I've done video yoga coaching with her many times. The beauty of putting work into the mind-body connection is that it's ageless and cumulative. She holds onto the incremental improvements and builds on them. The progress motivated my mother, and it motivated the people around her because her attitude changed. Now her body was a closer match to her brain, and if I didn't know her as I watched her doing yoga, I would not peg her at even close to seventy-seven.

I have a student who told me he was mourning the loss of his younger self. He's fifty-eight and in fantastic shape. I aspire to be that fit when I'm his age. Yet, he's disappointed. He clarified: for thirteen years, he was in a haze of drug use. He's feeling well enough now physically and mentally that he wishes he could have honored his body during that time the way he does now.

My student also regrets not maintaining the agility from his younger self. He feels like he just can't do everything that he used to be able to do. Given his physicality at close to sixty, I asked him to consider the possibility that when he was younger, he may have been able to perform physical feats, but it was accidental and unfocused. It might have been "messing around" without any discipline. Like me, unless he was training for the Olympics and had a team of coaches, he was likely not as agile as he thought he was. He was maybe less fearful, but maybe he was also sloppy and mindless. In addition to believing I was a great dancer in my teens, I remember being able to handspring from the living room ottoman and land on my feet. But how many times did I actually succeed? Maybe I focused on the achievements instead of the failures? I remember the one time when I was able to stand up on a sled the whole way down a snowy hill, but not the dozens of times I fell. I don't mourn the loss of that ability—I know it's still in me somewhere—I mourn the loss of that optimistic filter.

I suggested to my student that maybe he was mourning the loss of his perceived younger self. He's still him. It's still his body, and any concerns about loss of ability are addressed by working to regain it, and this time with intention and precision. When I practice with intention, it feels suddenly much harder, and seems like I've lost some ability. I haven't; I've gained awareness.

Like a tree's rings, my growth—experience and wisdom—is reflected in my body. Like everyone, living has taken a toll on me: broken bones, torn muscles, slipped discs, scarred and stretched skin, burns, wrinkles, bumps and bruises (not to mention my internal organs)! My life experiences have deepened my understanding of my limits, what works and what doesn't work for me. I wear my scars as a badge of honor, and as a reminder of my wisdom. Young students have the advantage of innocent resilience, and older students have the advantage of relaxed wisdom. Often, old and young dismiss each other. This is a loss.

**There's an opportunity on the mat, and in daily life, to reflect on what I've been to guide what I can become.**

## SIMPLICITY

I've thought about simplicity a lot in my design career. What is the simplest form for an on/off switch? What is the simplest way to avoid accidentally flipping that switch? What is the simplest arrangement of symbols and lines on an exit sign to make sure everyone escapes in an emergency?

Sometimes, I can arrive at a simple solution to a problem very quickly. But I've been taught that when I find a simple solution to something, I'm getting off easy and something must be wrong. Not true. Here's the reason: simple is often confused with easy, or half-assed. But easy is based on how quickly and effortlessly I can do something, without much thought to quality. Simple is based on results, and it still might take time.

Yoga has helped me understand this distinction. There are always simple ways to achieve yoga postures, but half-assed ways are impossible. I can't hide in a posture; either I've achieved a variation of the posture or I haven't...part way there isn't the posture. And I need to get to some form of the posture to reap the mental and physical benefits.

Yoga postures can be broken into a few main categories like balance, twisting, and bending. Most postures have overlapping categories, but each is biased toward one.

An example of a posture that looks like a confusing, complex, intimidating mess is *Eka Pada Koundinyasana*. In English, it's called flying splits. There is no easy way into this shape. It's an advanced posture, but in this case it's advanced because my brain needs to tackle it, not so much my body. Once I'm in the posture, not much strength or flexibility is required (Yes, this takes flexibility, but there's an adjustment to make the splits not so intense.)

This is a balance posture and I struggled with it, until one day my teacher said, "Why aren't you leaning forward more?" His tone was a mixture of empathy and incredulity that helped push the right button in my brain. By looking at me sweat and contort, he pinpointed exactly what I needed to do to achieve the posture. Granted, once I was there, it was rough and shaky and momentary, but I followed through and just needed to clean it up. Tipping my face forward and trusting my hands gave me a sudden sense of freedom and floating—another super-power uncovered.

This looks like a complex posture, with arms and legs supporting and twisting and extending in all directions. But it's not the appearance of the posture that I needed to be concerned with to achieve it; it's the simple idea that it's based in balance. There are many helpful ways into the posture, and those are basically ways to break down the problem into steps that happen to suit my particular body and brain, influenced by my own past experience. And this will not be achieved immediately and easily. But if I ask myself what's the simplest way to properly achieve something, I am using an approach that always works, whether I'm solving a life problem or working my way into a posture.

Now, for easy: I would not have succeeded if I had looked for an easy way to accomplish this posture. However, once I put the work into understanding the posture, and once I had the right muscle awareness and conditioning, I perceived the posture as easy.

Simplicity is valuable, and it takes work, and time. It's increasingly hard to lead a simple life, but if I'm consistent about breaking every challenge into basic components and asking myself what's the most efficient way to the desired outcome, the task of getting there is more focused, less burdensome, and most of the time far more successful.

**By striving for simplicity in my life, I'm ultimately making life easier too.**

## COMFORT

"Comfortable" is an uncomfortable word. It's supposed to mean "causing no pain". Painlessness is good! I strive for comfort. I want to sleep well and eat pleasant food. I want to be pain-free physically and mentally. I don't want nasty surprises. And I generally want to control the roller coaster of life as much as I can. For me, comfort also means security. The problem is, I very easily start to confuse "comfortable" with "familiar", and that's where things can get twisted. By subjecting myself to the same, familiar circumstances over and over, I can ironically find myself in a great deal of emotional or physical pain or both, the extraction from which is a challenging if not frightening prospect. Tickling is fun. Tickling too much draws blood.

But wait: exposing myself to the same thing for ten thousand hours…isn't that how someone becomes an expert? No—experts are people who have willingly subjected themselves to a thorough, far-reaching, full spectrum of experiences on a particular topic (possibly for ten thousand hours) so that when the need arises, they can draw from a vast reservoir of first-hand knowledge to solve a problem. An expert immerses themselves in unfamiliarity to become masterful.

**An expert finds comfort in the unfamiliar.**

When I teach a yoga class, I have a duty to make sure that students don't injure themselves. I watch their faces, I check in with them, I empower them to speak up (and no, I don't tickle them). But I also have a duty to make sure they're exposed to the unfamiliar. The breadth of yoga postures, combined with a bit of creativity, takes care of that, and I'll ease students into those unfamiliar postures step-by-step. But then, I present them with the abstract idea of finding comfort in a posture that to them at that point in time is incredibly uncomfortable. They're a mess, and I'm telling them that somewhere in that pool of sweat, fatigue, and disorientation is a sweet spot that they will come to see as effortlessness. Sometimes I can see them relax a little and still hold the posture, which means they're accepting the unfamiliar sensations and exploring them, as opposed to blowing past them. This takes a few sessions to achieve, and some sequenced physical conditioning leading into the posture is necessary to build strength and flexibility. But this is really the warm-up for the brain.

**Exposure to the unfamiliar is crucial in yoga. By association, this means it's also crucial to living.**

I'm only now able to understand first-hand what I was told years ago: yoga is designed to enable me to sit in stillness for long periods of time. With physical fitness comes the removal of distractions—discomfort—so that I can focus inward. That's yoga working from the outside in.

So I've become good at sitting by not sitting. I've found comfort in postures that at first were strange and grueling. In doing so, my body and mind gained a stamina and resilience that made sitting in stillness a type of controlled balance as opposed to a mindless slump.

Off the mat, comfort is just as elusive. We moved from Hong Kong to Los Angeles a few years ago, and despite having moved across the planet two years earlier from Boston, adapting to life in Los Angeles was rough. It was harder to make friends in Los Angeles; Hong Kong is filled with expats looking to connect, and I had the bonus of locals I had trained with who welcomed us into their social groups with open arms. Hong Kong is also all about good service and efficient logistics. When we moved back to North America, I experienced a reverse culture-shock.

I realized recently that a good deal of the struggle had been from trying to replicate the fantastic life in Hong Kong. For stupidly obvious reasons, this is wrong; Los Angeles is a different city, with different people and a different landscape. I had been looking for familiarity, when I really should have been looking for new things to absorb and appreciate.

The world changes around me constantly. My body and mind are constantly changing. I have no choice but to embrace unfamiliarity and search out the new things that make me happy and secure within those altered circumstances. Fortunately, the more I take this approach, the easier it gets to find comfort.

## CREATIVITY

My life is not a straightforward, black and white series of problems and solutions. To progress through a week socially and professionally, I need to be creative in ways beyond writing a funny message in a birthday card or coming up with a Hallowe'en costume. I often hear people declare, "I don't have a creative bone in my body!", which is impossible; creativity is something that all humans use to survive. A family struggling financially finds creative ways to keep the kids entertained and still put food on the table. Creativity is often confused with the skills that are used to execute ideas: drawing, building, making, decorating. Some of the most skilled artists or craftspeople can be surprisingly uncreative. Conversely, my brother owns a management consultancy that works with government agencies, which would seem to be an uncreative industry, yet he's one of the most creative people I know.

**Creativity is about more than flashy ideas: it's thinking broadly about a problem, intuitively formulating a series of solutions, and then stepping back and calmly using a set of rational filters to choose the right path.**

The more I practice my creative process, the stronger the solutions. Despite how 'the creative genius' is portrayed in popular culture amid a chaotic mess of papers, diagrams, and exhausted assistants, I've come to realize that my most inspired work—like figuring out how to get my car diagonally upward out of a snowbank on an icy hill—has been achieved during moments of calm, not chaos. The same is true on the yoga mat. I've tipped into advanced postures not by frantically contorting myself, but by breathing deeply, relaxing my brain, and pushing.

Sometimes, I have really good ideas when I'm taking a shower, doing dishes, or jogging. The repetitive, calming nature of these activities somehow opens a door, and I walk through and lose myself, just for a moment. I don't consciously decide, "Okay, I need to think through this problem." I'm relaxed and on autopilot with the task, and the thoughts just seem to appear over my shoulder. Hello! As it turns out, during these times my brain is producing alpha waves, similar to when I'm just gently waking or falling asleep: my blood pressure is low, my heart rate is slow, and my emotions are not guiding my thoughts. I've also often had good ideas in this state, as have many other people, hence the phrase "sleeping on it." I've usually already spent hours trying to work through the problem and solutions, and finally this mental state is where I achieve some clarity—the "aha" moment.

Here's a very simple flow to capture the creative process:

| | |
|---|---|
| **Inspiration** | **"Oh! Here's an idea!"** |
| **Chaos** | **"Look at all these options!"** |
| **Doubt** | **"This is all garbage!"** |
| **Clarity** | **"Ah, here it is."** |
| **Celebration** | **"I'm a genius!"** |

Clarity—the moment when the right idea appears, that I later consider brilliant—is always paired with equanimity. The other stages are emotional: confusing, joyful and frustratin challenge is to achieve the state of clarity and equanimity in a reliable, repeatable way. The key is to understand myself, to trust the process, and to practice.

The moment of clarity is when my mind is calm. There's a crucial period after doubt where many creatives have figured out ways to keep moving forward, despite an urge to quit. It's a state similar to the one that can be achieved on the yoga mat. It's a state of equanimity where I pull the reigns in on emotion, and the doubt or excitement dissolve, thereby enabling a clearer understanding of whether what's being created meets the goals I set out…in other words, if it's any good. I can only determine this with the haze of emotion cleared away, especially thoughts of creative genius.

When I've paid close attention to my own creative process, I've seen that the times of creative excellence have been calm, if only for a fleeting moment when the solution was formed. Then, the joy and rush of emotion have followed. A eureka moment is calm and austere. The joy and celebration are later, and sometimes only by a microsecond, which can make it seem that the idea and the excitement happened at the same time. The ideas formed during a frenzy of emotion are rarely good; I've produces pages of content in a burst of ego, only to look back later and wonder, "What was I thinking?"

My yoga practice enables a similar, controlled state of mind where alpha waves are produced. To be clear: inspiration does not strike me when I'm practicing yoga; the nature of the practice is for my mind not to wander. It's a process of smoothing out positive and negative emotions (equanimity) associated with the task at hand. Physical and mental distractions are systematically cleared away. With practice, I sustain this smoothness, and make progress from session to session. By strengthening my equanimity, yoga allows me to clear the way for ideas or solutions, and for the ability to evaluate whether they're any good.

**Alpha waves generated during a yoga practice are a result of breathing, movement, and focus. The mental state that is achieved is the context within which creative breakthroughs can happen.**

It's only from practicing yoga that I've realized that a creative breakthrough, like a physical breakthrough on the yoga mat, is a kind of transformation, and although it might seem sudden, it's gradual series of changes. Years of experience can make these changes more efficient, but they are still a necessary pathway to a solution. I need to trust this process and commit to it. There is no hiding on the yoga mat, nor is there when I must create something. Vulnerability and mindfulness in a yoga practice, or during the creative process, allow me to address my true self without emotion or judgement. Then, my progress is built on honesty, and it's sustainable.

# EGO

People mostly do what I tell them in a yoga session. This is a big responsibility. I have dreams where nobody is listening, and some are outright refusing to participate. This frightens me and makes me realize how much my ego is at play.

What does my ego want the most? To win. Not kept in check, this is a slippery slope to some unpleasant things. Depression and anxiety result from a stack-up of a lack of "wins". Or, if my ego does not get what it wants, it looks for other ways to impose itself: anger, frustration, self-sabotage and destruction. And yet, my ego helps to motivate me. It makes me want to improve myself. My ego can help me get things done, and to progress. In other words:

**My ego drives my good actions and my bad reactions.**

Ego gets me to my yoga mat, which is a good thing. I always have a number of postures that I'm working on. Most times that I'm on the mat, I get a little closer to accomplishing them, whether it's by gaining an insight on a small change of hand position to shift my weight for an arm balance, or through the sheer physical progress of strength and flexibility as I get farther into a backbend. I'm not comparing myself with others, I'm comparing my new accomplishments with past ones.

Sometimes ego gets me off my yoga mat, which is a bad thing. I have a choice when I become distracted by negative thoughts or encounter a problem with a posture: I can think, "Here we go. I haven't been working hard enough and it's showing. How can I possibly teach this posture if I can't even do it myself? I don't know what I'm doing. I've put in all this time and I'm nowhere near nailing it." Disappointment. Frustration. Fear. Disengagement.

Or, I can think, "Hmm. That's weird. I did this a few months ago. I know the breakdown and the preparation. I must be a little out of practice, so I'll have to figure out what's going on here and get that posture back. Here's one more useful, relatable challenge to convey when I teach this to my students." Vulnerability. Humility. Learning. Progress.

**Yoga has the dual function of humbling me and empowering me, as needed.**

My ego is even harder to reign in when there are other people involved. Then, I'm not just competing with myself to win—to do better this time than I did last—but competing with how I think other people perceive me and my abilities.

Here's a useful example:

I think I'm a good yoga teacher. I have proof: people keep coming back to my studio and my business has grown. Some students have completed hundreds of hours of training with me. They tell me I have helped them, and they've learned a lot. I can see it in them. They've told other people about my sessions and these new people have signed up. I have learned a lot and I use that knowledge to coach people in their practice.

And yet… once, one of my students, late to a session, walked in the door and told me that in his haste he had tripped on the steps into the studio and had jarred his whole body. I asked if he had injured himself, and he said no, he had just been shaken up. We did the session, and he left.

The next morning, I received an email from him that read:

*Hi - I just wanted you to know that session yesterday really did something to me, and I've been having back spasms since I woke up. I'm going to the doctor this afternoon. I don't know what else to do and I'm kind of worried.*

My reaction: "Whoa! He must think I'm a horrible teacher and that I don't know what I'm doing. He has mentioned back issues before, and I must not have been paying enough attention to his form. I've failed and guess that's it for me."

Then, my reaction shifted: "Wait, wait, wait. I know I didn't guide him into anything crazy last night. He has back spasms all the time. Why is he blaming me?! If anything, the yoga sessions have reduced the pain."

I did not reply to the email right away. I waited for my mind to stop spinning. I did some yoga.

With a clearer head, I remembered: he fell before he arrived. Besides, his email might simply have been to ask for help. My reply:

*Hi—that sounds awful. I remember you were quite jarred by your fall before the session. You said you were really tensed up. Generally, you've said the yoga has been helping your back, but let's wait to see what the doctor says and feel free to pop in here today or tomorrow and we can get you moving a bit to see how I can help.*

His response a few days later:

*Oh right—the fall. That's probably what did it. I feel fine now, BTW.*

There are so many things happening on both sides of this interaction, and they're all driven by ego. Blame. Shame. Fear. Anger. Once I stopped my reactions, and switched to actions, I was calm. I uncovered a possible source for his pain that was not from anything I had done. Once he received a nudge to consider the cause of his pain, he stopped reacting, maybe he relaxed, and maybe the pain even subsided. He has since continued to book weekly yoga sessions and has had some valuable breakthroughs.

This interaction reminded me that I can model behavior for others by how I manage my own ego. This way, there are no condescending or patronizing "teaching moments" because the connection is indirect and subtle, but also impactful and contagious.

My brother and I played tennis together as teens. The dynamic: if my brother missed a shot, he'd yell, dance around, throw his racket. Then he'd grit his teeth and aim to win the game at all cost. If I missed a shot, and had a sense that I was losing, especially if he had just lashed out and was hellbent on winning, I'd throw the game by acting like an idiot. Then, neither of us could claim the win. Smart, right?

My brother was allowing his ego to brutalize the game. I was letting my ego drive me away from the game. We learned nothing.

I hadn't played tennis for twenty years until I was at a party with friends, one of whom is a good tennis player. We had cocktails and rallied some balls. We were in flip flops. He missed some shots and laughed. I missed shots and witnessed my reactions from twenty years earlier starting to brew inside me. I was embarrassed, and then I started to joke around and wanted to stop. My friend had the ease and self-awareness I strive for on the yoga mat, and my reaction on the tennis court was still that of a fourteen-year old. The memories flooded back. Wow.

We did stop playing, but it was because food was ready. I was relieved. Upon reflection, the opportunity for such a direct application of what I've been cultivating on the yoga mat is rare, not to mention that I was able to compare my reaction now to similar circumstances from another period in my life. I'm glad this happened. Now I see tennis as a match of actions and reactions. I suspect the winners are the ones who let ego drive their actions, and not their reactions. I know this from my yoga practice. I may not ever win a tennis match, but now maybe I can deal with it like an adult! Yoga didn't make me a better tennis player, but it has shown me how perhaps I could be if I wanted to.

I think the biggest challenge for people starting a yoga practice is controlling ego. It's futile to try to put it aside. It's also hard to try to make it work constructively. Some people come to the mat expecting to use the same approach they do with lifting, running, visiting the dentist, or completing a report: muscle through to the end. Others are so fragile that the slightest missed expectation sends them reeling.

Not surprisingly, athletes I work with are very good about their egos—they're game, relaxed, consistent, and persistent. They get tired, but not emotional. Their ego filters the circumstances in the best possible way, taking a win as a win, and a loss as an opportunity to improve.

I don't care as much anymore about what others think of me. I worry about misunderstandings (maybe a little too much), but I don't speculate on how others perceive my ability or achievements. This is a tremendous relief. Yoga has given me this—a confidence that my honesty, gameness, and equanimity will carry me through a practice, and therefore will carry me through my daily tasks and interactions.

**After years of practice, I now let ego drive my actions, not my reactions. The challenge is to make sense of the difference.**

## GRATITUDE

At one end of the thankfulness spectrum, I consider that my parents created me and my world; they introduced me to its wonders and guided my reactions, but they've also literally created the mechanism in me that allows me to perceive it. Whether they did this consciously or not, this deserves some gratitude.

At the other, less spiritual end of the spectrum are all of the teachers, employers, friends, and colleagues who informed my development and helped me on my path. I cannot claim any bit of success without acknowledging them.

When I worked in the consulting world, I realized that a CEO rarely gets a thank you for being a good boss; expectations are the reverse. Staff are thanked. There may be leadership appreciation from afar, but it's rarely conveyed. If I truly feel that their work has benefitted me in some way, why not thank them?

Gratitude is also a practice of humility and honesty. This can of course mean thanking a higher power, but the risk is that this turns into a "chosen one" syndrome, which is unhealthy. Simply acknowledging that I did not get where I am completely on my own is what's important. There are lots of old-timey stories of self-made rags-to-riches people who triumphed despite all odds without help from anyone…and I just don't buy it. There's always someone who has helped, whether they know it or not. I'm wary of people who claim solo accomplishments.

**I am not a self-made person. Nobody is, and I challenge anyone who claims they are.**

It's been a very uncomfortable and humbling activity to list all of the people who have actively guided me, and how. Even harder is telling them, especially where some time has passed. Two years after changing jobs, my husband received a thank you note from a former staff member. He described how Duane's leadership had impacted him in ways that he did not understand or appreciate at the time. This was of course an ego boost to Duane that he rode on for days, and it was confirmation that his generosity with this struggling young designer was valuable. It was also behavior modeling that encouraged Duane to take stock of his own mentors. Similarly, this designer could have allowed the passage of time, since his contact with Duane, to convince himself that he had developed his new skills entirely on his own, but he chose not to.

**Bolstered by the generosity of others' gratitude toward me, I try to slip explicit, genuine thank yous into current interactions.**

I did not understand gratitude until I hit the yoga mat. I truly thought that to say I was not solely responsible for my own success was to admit weakness. Yoga has taught me that tiny prompts, gestures, or ideas from others can push me past my limits. I now see that's been happening my whole life, and acknowledging the help makes the help more valuable. Without understanding who or what has helped me, I don't understand how I've accomplished something. If I don't know the how, then I can't sustain the accomplishment, let alone advance beyond it. Gratitude is not about "counting my blessings because it could be worse". Gratitude is an act of self-reflection that enhances my identity and gives me a clearer understanding of my strengths, and more importantly my progress, by acknowledging what has enabled it. I take credit for amazing things that I've done, but I take that credit within the greater context of my circumstances, which includes other people.

Accomplishments aside, why am I so bad at accepting good things that happen from day to day? Every Friday (when we remember), my husband and I spend a few minutes talking about the good things from the week. Sometimes I think, "Well, I don't have anything good to list this week." But I do. Even the tiniest thing, like "I managed to unclog the vacuum hose" is worth mentioning. In fact, often it's only the small things that make it to the good list. This is an incredibly refreshing and mood-altering practice.

"Good" is in the details. I just need to dissolve my protective cynicism and look for it. It's easy to whip out my inner critic after a movie, a meal, or a party. But I've discovered it feels much better to simply sit back and say, "That was nice. I enjoyed it."

This is hard. Somehow, I've learned to pair good with bad. "I met a great new client yesterday," is normally "That new client seems nice, but we'll see if she comes back to the studio." Why? I might focus on the negative so that I can inoculate myself against future pain. But this is rarely the result; it just brings more negatives and I feel lousy. Decoupling good from bad, and if necessary, identifying absurdly insignificant positive events—"I enjoyed a glass of water today."—starts to rebuild my outlook. Once I start listing and accepting the good, it gets easier. Over time, I feel less burdened. Lighter. Gratitude also reveals where I might need to make a change. If I feel that things are not going according to plan, if I'm suffering, my inability to be grateful tells me that maybe I need to find another path.

Yoga is my filter. I would not have a practice, nor would I be as fit or as sane, if I did not have access to great teachers. I am grateful for them. Yoga has been the most explicit proof of the impact of others on me. I did not "figure out" yoga on my own, and it would be absurd to claim this, although many make such claims in other industries.

Yoga has shown me that it's not just big transformations that are deserving of gratitude, nor does the expression of that gratitude need to be a grand gesture. It can be small and quiet. On the mat, freed from daily patterns of behavior, I've learned to look for the success that's unique to me: stepping my foot an inch closer to my hand, holding my balance for a breath longer, making the time for myself to get on the mat in the first place. If I pause to reflect on how far I've progressed, and with whose help, I'm embracing the idea that I can progress further.

## SNEAKINESS

Some people are literally, knowingly sneaky. I know this because I used to be sneaky too. I grew up lying. I pretended to be sick to avoid going to school. I lied to avoid getting in trouble with teachers. I pretended to be straight to avoid the turmoil of coming out of the closet. In the early years of owning a corporation, when managing customer service issues like late shipments, my problem-solving inclination was to lie. Lying was so much a part of my mode of operating that I often didn't know I was doing it.

My vulnerability on the yoga mat has helped me to stop being a liar. There's no hiding from the reality of where I am in my practice; it's visible to everyone, and I can feel it myself. I've discovered that honesty helps me progress.

I see this in students as well. It's not always conscious. My job is to gently point out the areas of vulnerability—where maybe they're inclined to "cheat"—so that we can get real work done. This does not always get a good reaction, and at times, though rarely, a student is so uncomfortable with the unexpected exposure that they never come back to my studio, which is unfortunate. In these cases, it might be the discomfort of realizing they're going to have to work hard, and that I can't do it for them, that pushes them away. But I have the confidence from my experiences in my own practice and do my best to reassure students that they will improve. Over time, an honesty appears in their body, fidgeting dissolves, and I can see their dedication through the precision and control in their movements. They're unburdened from the reflex of trying to find a way out, a way to cheat, and they're just doing it.

A simple example of the sneakiness of my body and brain is when I'm in a forward bend.

I try to keep my knees straight, but there's discomfort in my hamstrings. The automatic, and sneaky, solution is to pop my knees forward to bend them just a little, to relieve the pain. I usually don't even realize I'm doing it—my legs still feel straight. People do this all the time on the mat, even more advanced students in complex postures, and I have to remind them, "You can straighten your legs. They're being sneaky." A minute later, they're bent again.

I can control some things in my body and brain, and others I cannot. Over time, I've gained control over the things that I didn't think were controllable, and also achieved a sense of awareness and acceptance of the things that I've realized I can't control. This might sound familiar:

> **"God, grant me the serenity to accept the things I cannot change, courage to change the things I can, and the wisdom to know the difference."**

This is called *The Serenity Prayer*. I call it the Sneakiness Prayer.

Yoga helps me understand this, using simple breathing and movement: I cannot stop breathing, but I can control the speed and depth of my breath. I cannot change the basic structure of my bones and muscles, but I can gain the strength and flexibility to make the most of the body that I have. I cannot stop the passage of time, but I can filter the effect of my surroundings on my body and mind to stay engaged, mobile, and happy, in effect aging differently from how generations before me did.

## Yoga makes me vigilant.

Basically, yoga helps me be mindful of when my body and mind are working in unison, and when they're fighting each other. The more I tap into this vigilance, the easier it gets to see a mind-body discord. Each yoga posture, however simple it may seem, is vastly loaded with potential adjustments. These tiny changes are based on general "how to" information and industry insights, but more importantly are from my own awareness of how I feel in that posture, physically and mentally. This also applies to a simple posture change when I'm sitting at my desk, a simple change to my breathing when I'm feeling stressed, or a simple change to how I interact with someone in a difficult situation. My deepened self-awareness keeps my mind and body from being sneaky.

Vigilance begets vigilance. I tell my students this, and what at first seems like meaningless rolling dialogue describing the opportunities they have to adjust their bodies and attitudes with each posture (one of my students once said I sound like an auctioneer) turns into an affirmation of what they're discovering. At first, they don't believe me; then they're astonished. They stop listening to me and start listening to themselves.

## VULNERABILITY

On the yoga mat, I need to be vulnerable. Otherwise, I cannot transform. To be vulnerable is not to be fragile or weak, it's to be honest about where I am, and where I need to go. It's like being lost in a city and willing to ask someone for directions. Some people don't like that at all—they do everything they can to avoid it: get frustrated, angry, and closed off, they lash out or simply claim they're not interested in the opportunity at hand in the first place.

The first step of yoga—signing up for a class, rolling out a mat, taking shoes off—is a very revealing moment. Often, people don't make it even that far. Sometimes, people make it to the mat, but when faced with the reality of not being able to do a particular posture—finding themselves vulnerable—the session ends. What started as a simple goal of strengthening their back turns into a deeper exploration of their personality, and they're startled by that reality. All I'm doing is sitting and watching them, with periodic adjustments to their posture. Their understanding of where they're strong, where they're weak, and where they need to be flexible, literally and figuratively, is cast aside, and they need to rebuild. My job as a teacher is to guide them through their vulnerability, and to help them to get comfortable with it so that they can progress.

I didn't realize I was sharing and accepting my vulnerability in yoga until quite a while into my practice; there were postures to accomplish, and I enjoyed the process. The vulnerability was a side effect that snuck in when I struggled and, upon reflection, taught me valuable lessons for my behavior in real life: I can only identify and tackle obstacles if I allow myself to be vulnerable.

When I was younger, I needed everything to be perfect, including people's perceptions of me. During the hardest times—coming out, going through a financial crisis, discovering I had a heart condition—I maintained such a good 'game face' that friends and family didn't realize anything was wrong. In fact, many people saw my behavior as distant, disengaged and even arrogant. But then these crises got so bad it became impossible to hide anything. The emotional exposure explained a lot to loved ones and given the outpouring of support, I wish I had come clean sooner. I wish I'd had the courage to say, "I'm a mess. I need help."

In my own teaching, I've realized I can't assume that if I stick to describing the postures, adjustments, and benefits, I'm doing my job well. I need people to open up, but in a very specific way. This presents a challenge for me—I'm not a therapist, and must not dole out life advice. As humans, we want to connect and to make each other feel better during a crisis. If a student does become emotional about a personal problem while practicing, my task is to keep the physical session on track, having listened to and acknowledged their outpouring. I know the physical practice will help them sort things out mentally. This sometimes feels dismissive, but we're still engaged in dialogue; only it's a wordless one that uses the physical practice as an alternate path to finding and addressing their trauma. They've shown vulnerability simply by being on the yoga mat, and I need to encourage, respect, and protect that act.

**Now, I see that one of the most generous things I can give myself, friends, and even my students is vulnerability.**

Unburdening myself of the effort to hide things does not mean dumping my problems on others. Vulnerability spans my hopes, fears, problems and aspirations, the good and the bad, the ideas and the complaints. Being vulnerable simply means thinking about and sharing the particulars of my humanity to find common ground and strength.

## TRUST

What is trust? Trust in myself is confidence that stems from self-awareness. Trust in someone else is a belief that they know what they're doing, and that they'll do what they say. But do they know what's best for me? Are they even concerned with that? As a result, this kind of trust is very fragile. To trust someone, I need a deep enough knowledge myself of the subject at hand, an understanding of my limitations, and a pain-free, prior track record with that person. Before yoga, I tended to see trust as a gut-feeling, and now I see it as one more thing that's rooted in calm, analytic self-awareness.

**I need to trust myself before I can trust anyone else.**

In university, I had a brilliant professor who confided in me that when she created her exams, she gave students something easy, sometimes absurdly so, at the beginning to relax them and make them feel they could tackle the exam. She reduced anxiety by encouraging them to trust themselves, despite possible fear of the unknown, or of failure.

I teach yoga in much the same way. I start with simple, easy movements, and gradually build up to more challenging ones. Even with advanced students, breaking a complex posture into component parts is an opportunity to ease them into it, and also to show the posture in a simpler, more palatable way.

In yoga, trust extends beyond me to include the practice itself. I need to trust the process. Yoga has been around for millennia, and as a system, it works. Acting as a guide or a spotter, my teacher is not there to carry me, nor to be followed blindly. It's my responsibility to filter their guidance, hold on to what serves and enlightens me at that point in my life, and set the rest aside. There's a fine line between relinquishing control (which I must do sometimes) and blind faith (which never works). I've been in yoga training sessions where the duration and intensity forced me to relinquish control so fully that by the end, I barely knew up from down. All of my notions of how my body worked had been thrown out the window. But this was a process of relearning, and it was not enabled by blind faith. From my own past experiences, I trusted that I would make it through the training, and I had to remind myself that I had the capacity to grow. "Faith in the process" from my earlier design career, where a dedication to research, discovery, and iteration would render positive results, turned into "faith in the practice" with a similar approach: explore, reflect, and repeat.

Sometimes, if students are struggling, I'll ask them if they trust themselves. This usually triggers a quick self-check, where what they're really doing is reminding themselves that this whole experience has little to do with me as their teacher. At times I'll say "trust your hands" or "trust your feet" during balance postures as a way to get people out of their heads and to redirect their attention away from me and to focus on their body as a tool. When a breakthrough happens, which it always does, I'll remind them of the

process it took to get them there, and how over time they've gained confidence.

It's been helpful for me to consider the idea that third-party trust—the times when it's about someone else carrying out a task —is an illusion: it's not that I trust or don't trust that person. It's that I'm grappling with trusting myself. What's the worst that will happen if they mess it up? How will I deal with the consequences? Will I be able to manage? If they succeed, will I be jealous? If I've been the one training them, have I done a good enough job? If I've had nothing to do with the circumstances, and the situation is not in my control, am I worried that if there's a catastrophic result I won't have the skill or confidence to sort out the aftermath?

People will make mistakes. I will make mistakes. But I'll eventually get it right, and so will others. As long as everyone is sticking to a process and not being reckless, I can have faith in that process and know that the result will be successful. I owe this to my peers; I just need to be aware of my own abilities and limitations to proceed, especially with something new. Trust in myself is confidence, and that trust dissolves fear of my own and others' failure.

## PERFECTION

I once rolled pasta by hand with a friend, and each time his noodles were slightly flawed, he wanted to start over. I thought he was being ridiculous. We were just going to eat this, after all.

I had the honor once of making pottery with a Japanese master outside of Tokyo. My soft clay bowl flopped on the wheel. He would not let me restart. Instead, he carefully removed it from the surface and put it aside. Weeks later, I received a glazed, fired, beautifully imperfect bowl in the mail. It's impossible to put anything in the bowl, let alone wash it, but I prize it.

**Perfectionism stifles mastery.**

A husband and wife came to my studio for a private session a while back, and they wanted to work on balance. I have found balance sessions to be the most revealing in terms of personality; frustration and laughter emerge in parallel, and I have to work hard to keep people on track. This couple felt foolish for falling over in what they thought were going to be very easy postures, and when they started to get tired, the laughter turned to head shaking, frowning, and some anger and discouragement. Watching them, I realized their particular problem wasn't the balance per se, it's that they were restarting each time their sequence got even a little shaky. They wanted to be perfect, and because the session was a mini workshop without the constraints of a large class, they had the freedom to be compulsive. They were tiring themselves out, and not improving.

I suggested they simply continue with the sequence, regardless of how messy it got, and finish. This did the trick. They hopped around a little, waved their arms, almost lost their balance, but they completed it. Their brains were satisfied, and they relaxed. I had them do it one more time, and to everyone's amazement, the sequence was much smoother.

**Perfectionism is a compulsive excuse for leading a life of incomplete experiences.**

Sometimes I'll ask students to put less physical effort into their practice. This is challenging for most because they see it as me asking them to underperform. But I'm really asking them to perform differently. It's a kind of precise laziness, and interestingly, when they do it, their form is just as good if not better than when all the effort goes in. Their brain relaxes. Without the distraction of physical exertion, they can turn inward a little more easily, and really identify where the work needs to be put in. By changing their understanding of success, they're dissolving an expectation of perfection.

My idea of what I expect to be perfect and what I don't is different from everyone else's; I didn't care about the pasta, but I did care about the pottery. The couple was hell-bent on not looking stupid, but instead wound up looking crazy. Ego drives my particular version of perfectionism, and sometimes it's so overwhelming that I don't even try something in the first place. Social media are culprits here too. I rarely see a photo or video of someone humbled by their missteps, unless the point is comedy. It's all bright, smiley success; bruised egos and bodies are hidden from view.

My pottery experience, among other brushes with the art world, helped to show me that imperfection is far richer and broader as a source of discovery than perfection. It's inspiring to see a true artist at work, someone who is so deeply aware of their own process of discovery that they rejoice in errors, because it's from that misstep, or accident, that a gem can emerge.

If from time to time my yoga practice is shaky, I follow through, however messy, because there's always a chance to clean up and to refine the next time around. And, like in art, there might be a discovery in the sloppiness—a new technique, a new idea, that I would otherwise have missed.

**If I let go of perfection, I open myself to a myriad of new paths, all of which have useful obstacles that will broaden my experience and get me closer to mastery.**

## SPIRITUALITY

I'm guilty of liberal cynicism. I claim open-mindedness yet I'm so committed to science and facts that many aspects of spirituality and mystery are cast aside because there is no western, empirical evidence of function or benefit. In tandem, the human rights violations, exclusion, corruption, and even violence espoused by some organized religions—supposed center points to spirituality—are good reasons to steer clear.

And yet, there are still many inexplicable things in and around me. We recently had dinner with very good friends, and the subject of afterlife and higher power came up. Our friends' tone suggested an assumption: that everyone at the table shared the same view that there were no such things. I found myself embarrassed but compelled to say that I do believe in powers greater than us; we simply don't know, and isn't life more interesting this way? Unfortunately, the conversation did not continue on that topic. On a separate occasion, another good friend made a profound remark. she's a massage therapist who has started to explore more spirit and energy-based forms of healing, and she told me that she has stopped preceding talking about this with "I know this is going to sound crazy, but…" I very much appreciate the change to how she describes her journey.

One friend summarized the need to accept things outside of easy explanation by pointing at the placebo effect. "How is it," he asked, "that we accept that placebos often work in much the same way as actual medication, yet dismiss other inexplicable effects from non-western medicine as hocus-pocus?" Western medicine and religion in some ways have become perverted to serve profit. I've learned from newer data and scandals to be skeptical of the institutions I was raised in—church services and pediatrics (How do they know what happens when I die? What do they know about nutrition?)—but, paradoxically, I fear the alternatives because the proponents are mostly dismissed as kooks.

I have rituals without being religious. I repeat patterns of actions, thoughts, and behaviors to find comfort during difficult times, and to celebrate wins. Certain things are sacred to me, like my yoga practice. I see the personal benefits, and they go beyond physiological well-being. My yoga practice has reminded me of an innocent spirituality from my childhood, a time when it was okay to be in awe of the wonders of living and of nature, to not need an empirical explanation and to simply explore and accept my place in this complex, organic, and mysterious system.

**It's arrogant and narrow-sighted to think that spirituality cannot play a part in my wellness.**

The roots of ritual, of prayer, of meditation are in well-being. If there's an opportunity to look at all avenues to fix something in me that is broken, or to expand something that is budding, I will take it.

## FEAR

For me, fear is rooted in memories of pain. It might be physical pain, or it might be mental pain, and the fear of pain might even be triggered by something that I'm experiencing for the first time. Fear of change, newness, or unfamiliarity—the unknown—even with no past experience with the specific "new thing", can merely be based on a painful experience with something else that was new. I might attribute food poisoning to a new restaurant, and therefore I'm wary of trying another new restaurant. I know many self-described "creatures of habit", and I suspect what motivates them is not an appreciation for sameness, as the label suggests, but a fear of change. I had dinner with a colleague who visibly flinched when he noticed that the bread basket delivered to the table had focaccia speckled with olives, and from his expression for the next fifteen minutes I could tell it was so out of the ordinary for him that it was all he could think of. He wanted bread, but he did not want weird bread.

**Fear isn't just hard to admit, it's hard to identify.**

When I'm scared of something, I ask myself: do I know that this will cause me pain? If it might, I can choose to avoid it, and sometimes, rationally, that's the best thing to do. Alternatively, I can deepen the inquiry: What are the chances of more pain this time, and how bad might it be?

Around 2005, when my husband and I were running our business, we encountered a back-to-back series of catastrophic errors that put our business (and therefore everything we owned) in jeopardy. This was the first time I had ever encountered such deeply negative emotions. I was angry and frightened. I would wake up with my heart pounding, and felt paralyzed and without options. One late afternoon when we got home from work, I sat on the steps, looked at Duane, and said, "I'm worried I'm going to die." I started to cry. The emotions and their physical manifestation in me were so strong and unfamiliar that the stress was essentially doubled. I was worried not only about the business predicament, but what it was doing to me. It was difficult for Duane to console me because on the one hand it was such a dramatic statement that he was not equipped to respond, and on the other hand, he likely felt the same way since we were both going through the same thing.

I did not have a yoga practice at the time. Now, I have a practice, and although I've been in similarly stressful circumstances, I'm not affected even closely to the same degree. The years that have passed since then have given me wisdom, so I can't attribute my resilience entirely to yoga, but I will say that the systematic nature of yoga has equipped me to manage crises in much the same way that I manage challenging postures on the mat: with perseverance and grace.

I also say this with a degree of sobriety: yoga does not solve all world problems, and I'm not suggesting that people in war-torn countries could stem the onslaught of damaging, negative, horrifying emotions triggered by the tragedies they encounter by doing some yoga. That's nonsense.

Fear is useful as a self-preservation tool. There's a fine line between fearlessness and recklessness; we laud fearless people, but this can often lead to injury or disaster. I live in a safe bubble where at times I can ignore that distinction. On the battlefield, a soldier cannot be reckless, and fear must be managed, not ignored. A mindful acknowledgement of fear will lead to much more positive, sustainable results.

Everyone deals with fear differently. On the mat, I see fear in myself and in others in certain poses, like handstands, backbends, and deep stretches. But I also see it in less obvious poses, like lying on the floor in savasana, or even just sitting quietly. Some people recoil and avoid scary situations; some people grit their teeth and muscle through them. Some people react with anger and lash out, and some people become depressed. All reactions are normal and serve a purpose, but they can also get in the way of growth. The advantage during a yoga practice is that there's an opportunity to address the fear in a safe, controlled, repeatable way.

Yoga has built my physical and mental confidence, and has helped me pinpoint what is triggering my fear in most cases during my practice: failure and vulnerability. I recently had a student who began to cry during a one-on-one session. He did not want to be there, and he confided in me that it was because he was scared of failing.

I learned in corporate terms to "fail well and often" so that I can learn and then succeed. But this is stressful, and now I find quite misleading. The risk with this approach is that it tells me it's important to fail (which it is not) and that success is the goal, and therefore the ceiling of my progress. I've started to consider the idea that failure and success are not a thing; it's not about whether I fail or succeed, but how close I can get to accomplishing my goals. Any amounts of effort and accomplishment are valuable; there is no such thing as failure. This is an important distinction to make. It helps to remove expectations, but still motivates me to progress. This is fundamentally what the corporate speak is intending as well, but in overly simplistic terms.

**The essence of 'failing well and often' is to be mindful of what is working and what is not, to understand why, and to move forward.**

When I'm upside-down in a yoga posture, I'm afraid of falling over. I don't have a good sense of where the ground is. It's unfamiliar, so I practice. This process dampens the fear of the unknown because it builds self-trust. How will I tackle this new set of tasks I've been given? How will I behave on this date or interview or trip? How will I do a handstand without falling over? I'll trust myself to follow the same methodical process I always do, and I'll be calm, and I'll figure it out.

**In a challenging posture, I might fall over. But the ground is not as far as I think.**

Yoga has helped me learn to manage fear. That means first identifying that I'm scared, what I'm scared of specifically, and then finding a path through it.

## CONFIDENCE

I find confidence in truth and knowledge. I've learned confidence does not mean always pushing forward with the set of skills that I am comfortable with. It means relying on the tools that I have to filter new experiences so that I can move forward with an even deeper self-awareness.

I'm tuned in to my surroundings, and I listen. If I hear feedback from someone, however negative or positive it might be, I consider what they've said. Is it something that I can learn from, that can help transform me? Is it something that will hinder my transformation?

**To be confident, I need to be willing to learn.**

On the yoga mat, blind or "false" confidence can be dangerous for teachers and students. Doing a forearm balance with no trust in my own skills, purely for the sake of show, can put me out of commission. The same is true in social or work settings, where the negative effects of false confidence might not be as apparent as a sprained shoulder but can be far more destructive.

In the early 2000s, when Duane and I started our company, our first hire was a woman who appeared to have all the qualities we needed as a head of sales: personable, quick-witted, and efficient. We trusted her with a large number of important responsibilities, with the idea that as more people were hired, her role would become more targeted to what she had been hired for: customer relations and sales. At first, she excelled. But as our company grew, and her real role coalesced for her as promised, things started to erode. She became irritable and secretive, and she would cut check-ins short claiming she was far too busy to pull together reports; "I need to sell!", she'd say.

It became clear to us soon enough: now that her job required her to do what she claimed was her expertise, she didn't know what she was doing. Unfortunately, rather than be honest and ask for help learning, she continued to flounder, taking some of our accounts down with her. Her eventual departure was a relief to us as well as other staff members who had been sidelined in her attempts to maintain the illusion of confidence. We never truly understood what drove her. Was it ego? Fear? Both?

Since then, I've heard many stories from others about similar workplace frustrations where even company leadership had no aptitude for their job. How did they get hired? False confidence. Some people are masters at convincing others that they know what they're doing, while they are novices at their actual tasks. This is not sustainable.

A firefighter cannot rush into a burning building without equipment and training. Actors improvising onstage appear to have a vast sense of confidence that might seem false—no script, no plan—but they have years of experience in doing just that. They are trained to be comfortable in a situation that would paralyze most people, and they deliver.

**Yoga is the place to experiment with my sense of confidence. On the mat, I'm the only one injured by false confidence; off the mat, I risk taking others down with me.**

If I feel even a little bit of anxiety when working through a yoga posture, it tells me that something is lacking in my knowledge and experience, which is therefore where I should be putting in the work. The longer I "pull it off" without doing the work, the more dramatic the failure. My face will meet the yoga mat, so to speak, and I'll wind up bruised inside and out. The encouraging news is that once I've committed to digging deep and really learning something, the time it takes to establish real, honest confidence is relatively short.

## SELF-AWARENESS

I've realized through yoga that self-awareness doesn't mean to know my boundaries and to stick within them, but to know what drives me, my strengths and my weaknesses, and to use that to transform myself.

On the yoga mat, everything is in my control. I don't need weights, rackets, or shoes. I don't need to go anywhere. Focusing on my body for even five minutes reinforces my capacity to be my own boss.

How do I feel? Now, I feel good. But for many years I was operating on a baseline of feeling mediocre and didn't know any better. Early in my yoga training, I attended a five-day retreat to learn about the role of yoga in physical and mental therapy. Most of the other attendees were older and more experienced teachers. During meals, I'd often hear a few talking about how the food from the previous meal had affected them. They were out of their eating routines, and because of a combination of jetlag and a heavy practice and theory schedule, they felt out of sorts. I did not understand this. Now I do. What I saw in yoga practitioners as a sensitivity to food, drink, and environment—a general lack of resilience—I now realize is an understanding that they can, and want to, feel better. They do not accept the baseline, and they're pushing themselves for better circumstances. What I saw in my younger body as a "forgiving" physiology— I could operate on less sleep, and eat and drink poorly—was actually poor self-awareness. I had operated that way for so long I didn't know any differently.

How did I arrive at this through yoga? The nature of a yoga

practice—inquiry, experimentation, reflection—is ultimately intended to help me understand how my mind and body work, so that I can feel better. And feel better I do: holistically from year to year my physical and mental health have improved, and I function better as a person.

I know what it's like to feel good now, and I stay away from the things that prevent that. I can read articles and follow expert recommendations, but my baseline of "good" is unique to me, ever-increasing, and only achieved through an understanding of my limits, tendencies, and preconceptions.

## AWARENESS PRACTICE

Sit on the ground.
Bow my head.
Close my eyes.
Take five deep breaths.
Lift my head.
Open my eyes and look around.
Put my hands on the ground in front of me.
Look at my hands.
Wiggle my fingers.
I did that.
Sit up straight.
Take a deep breath through my nose.
Smell.
Close my eyes.
Listen.
Put a hand on my heart, and one on my stomach.
Feel my breathing and my heartbeat.
Open my eyes.
Stand up slowly, one movement at a time.
Raise my arms over my head and stretch upward.
Inhale.
Lower my arms back down to my sides.
Exhale.
I did that.
Smile.
I am, mind and body, in this world.

# LET'S FINISH

My yoga practice is about me. Nobody else. I'm not worshipping anybody. I'm not working on the mat to directly improve my relationship with anybody. I'm not on the mat to solve any world problems. Technically, I'm being selfish. But that's not a bad thing; it's self-improvement that does not harm anyone or take anything away from them. The beauty of a yoga practice is that ultimately, my un-monstering is in service of others.

Yoga as a selfish practice does have a dark side: I could be on the mat at the expense of spending time with family and friends, or as a way to avoid facing problems. And this does happen: devotion to a practice can become distorted or perverted where the ultimate goal of being a better person and interacting more happily with surroundings takes a second seat to the practice itself. It has happened to me. Early in my training I was taking up to three classes a day, which basically ate up all my time. When I missed one, I worried I was lacking some crucial piece of wisdom that everyone else was getting. This was a slippery slope to compulsion, and luckily my husband had the objectivity to gently set me straight.

Any posture that I work on has two variables: my body and my mind. With conditioning, the physical obstacles dissolve, leaving only those in my mind. I have to face the psychological manifestation of physical obstacles—fear, frustration, impatience, dissatisfaction, weakness, imbalance, lethargy—to proceed with the session. A good teacher will act as my guide, a kind of non-verbal therapist to gently coax me into making adjustments to my practice and trying new things. The obstacles will surface and over time will dissolve as I gain confidence. My sense of self—my understanding of how I work—will deepen, and I'll apply what I've learned on the mat to my daily life. This allows me to more clearly see my place in the world.

I hear about all the big ideas out there to make society better. Space travel. Self-driving cars. Smart homes. Lotteries. Stuff. These things might make daily life easier, but not necessarily better. The change has to happen inside me.

At times, I've returned home after buying some new clothes or some electronics, and just sat on the sofa a little disappointed and deflated... maybe even a little guilty. But I've found that when my body and mind are in balance—exercised and content—I'm no longer looking for external solutions beyond fulfilling basic needs of food, clothing, and shelter for me and my family. I've deepened my appreciation for smaller pleasures, somewhat like the refreshed palate of someone who recently quit smoking and is suddenly tasting and smelling food more deeply: it's richer, more sensual. I see people around me differently as well. Their, at times, bad behavior hasn't changed, but my perception of it has and it seems less significant.

**Empathy and compassion are enabled by my nurtured self.**

Trying to find meaning in yoga and its connection to life is hard work, and very personal. Things that I used to see as solutions I now see as band-aids, or even distractions. I've discovered my "smooth self"—something beneath the rippling layers of emotion and distraction—is unwavering and reliable. It has low blood pressure. It loves and is loved. It is strong and eager. Yoga is dissolving the layers a little more every day to get my conscious mind closer to that smooth self and enriching my daily activities along the way.

At a family party one day, I was having a conversation about blood pressure (mine runs high) with one of my husband's uncles. He's very liberal and thoughtful, and asked me if it's possible that my blood pressure is high because I'm gay. This was not an insensitive question. I understood his point: is it high because I've had to constantly filter myself, mask myself, to feel safe? Is my blood pressure high sometimes because I'm not being myself? I think he's right. I feel the most secure and comfortable in the times when I'm surrounded by people who know and love me for who I am. Otherwise, there's a constant, low-level stress that harms me. But I cannot always avoid stressful interactions outside of my bubble; the best I can do is to build resilience and self-awareness to dampen them and to recover quickly, in effect smoothing out the bumps.

In very simple terms, yoga—the reflection, the experimentation, the learning—has reminded me of childhood, before the circumstances, peers, and expectations of adulthood took hold. I often ask people what their "job" was when they were five years old, before they were swayed by circumstance. That is a beautiful reminder of what's under all the obfuscating layers that age and time have created. I need to be doing even just a bit of what I did at age five to achieve an honesty, to rediscover my underlying self.

If I can separate my understanding of my "self" from the limitations of my body and mind, then I can see that my "self" is the "wisdom" so to speak, that is ever-deepening and never subject to the corrosive effects of daily life. Teaching a physical practice requires me to be analytical and clear, which can seem at odds with the abstract nature of the "self". But it's not; I've made these discoveries in my own practice—experimenting with my mind and my body on a yoga mat—and I can help guide others the same way to deepen their self-awareness.

**When I'm at service to myself,**
**I'm at service to others.**

I am occupying space in this world, and there are many other people. I have inherent value and am entitled to happiness. I have a function, and even during times of greatest doubt, I am still necessary and must not squander my existence. What at one point can seem like a hopeless low can very quickly flip to a high, and I need to be equipped to see, to manage, and to make the most of the transformation when it's afoot. I need to bring my self into focus during the worst and best of times, because it's this dedication that will optimize my role and usefulness in the world.

And the same is true for you: you're important and valuable in ways you might not even know yet. I hope some of the stories and observations of my own monsterhood resonate well and are helpful to you on your journey!

Thank you for spending time with me.

## CHEAT SHEET

The following will help you hold your own at a party when the topic of yoga comes up:

1. Yoga is a practice. It's an experiment in patience, stamina, and self-awareness.
2. A yoga practice works from the outside in and the inside out.
3. The state of my body affects my mind. Conversely, my mind can affect my body—hence illness from stress.
4. Distractions can take many forms: injury, illness, negative thoughts, or discomfort. Yoga is a systematic way to remove distractions from the body and mind.
5. A good yoga practice is thorough; it addresses and rebalances all body parts, thereby addressing all corners of my mind.
6. Yoga builds resilience in the body and mind by developing strength and flexibility.
7. Environments, relationships, bodies, and minds are always changing, and a yoga practice can be an anchor in this sea of flux.
8. Transformation is the result of tiny, incremental changes.
9. To learn is to change. Physical and mental fitness are not sustainable without learning.
10. Yoga is a rare opportunity to be selfish.

## ACKNOWLEDGEMENTS

Special thanks go to my family and friends, not only for providing the nurturing life experiences that led me down this path, but also for their patient conversations and willing reviews of drafts of this manuscript: my husband Duane Smith, my brother Denis Barbeau, my sister-in-law Alexei O'Connor, Rachel Welch, Tracy Swyst, Melanie Cheng, Chris Johns, Martin Yeeles, Edmond Sanctis, Ken Jewell, Anne Marie Stein, David Hurwitz, Corbin Smith, Paul Desany, Will Cokeley, and Tracey Alf. Special thanks go to Hugh Jarrett for his repeated reviews, suggestions, and his attention to detail.

Thank you to my parents, Brigitte and Victor, for their unwavering support, including letting me be a princess for Halloween at the age of five.

I want to express my deep gratitude to my teachers, Sudhakar Dheenan from Vanakkam Yoga School, and Ganesh Mohan from Svastha Yoga and Ayurveda, as well as to all my yoga mates and students!

# ABOUT THE AUTHOR

After spending decades working as an award-winning industrial designer, Stefane abruptly moved to Asia to study yoga for two years. Thousands of teaching hours later, he now coaches people in his private studio, Clinic Yoga, to find strength, flexibility, and balance in their own lives. He is also the founder of designleadership.clinic, and conducts workshops around the world to show that creative problem solving, like yoga, is about process and practice.

Stefane lives in Palm Springs, California with his calm husband Duane, and their neurotic pit bull, Sally.

CPSIA information can be obtained
at www.ICGtesting.com
Printed in the USA
BVHW042019080422
633693BV00003B/8